Design and Build a
SPORTS CAR

Stuart Mills

First published 2013

Copyright Performance Publishing Ltd

ISBN 978-0-9576450-0-4

Published by **Performance Publishing Ltd**
Unit G, Acorn Business Centre, Livingstone Way,
Taunton, Somerset TA2 6BD

Author: Stuart Mills
Editor: Adam Wilkins
Graphic Design and Print: Panda Creative Ltd

DISCLAIMER

Whilst every effort has been taken to ensure the accuracy of the
information given in this book, no liability can be accepted by the
author, publisher or distributor for any loss, damage or injury caused
by errors in, or omissions from, or misuse of the information given.

About The Author

STUART MILLS WAS born in Nottingham in 1958, and developed an interest in mechanical engineering at a very early age. At six, his dad showed him how to use tools in the shed, and together they made a trolley, or soapbox, as they were called. This gave Stuart an appetite for understanding all vehicles. He made a unicycle at the age of 10, ventured further with the soapbox idea and made his first electric vehicle with a lorry starter motor at the age of 12. Stuart then moved to cycling, and spent three years training and racing, ultimately becoming Nottinghamshire Schoolboy Champion in the 10-mile time trials of 1973.

The lure of petrol was too great to resist, however, and at 16 he quickly became known as 'Mr Fix It' on the housing estate where he grew up, and spent most of his spare time repairing mopeds and scooters. Stuart's first job was with his dad who taught him many of the engineering skills that are now invaluable to him. The job involved repairing and modifying industrial sewing machines and, not content with following tradition, Stuart used his creative abilities to design and develop garment conveyors, innovative vacuum assisted steam pressing tables and steam generators. He also worked as a DJ at the Nottingham Palais and as a singer and bass player in many bands.

His other passion remained vehicles, and at the first Newark kit car show, in the early 1980s, he purchased a T-Bucket body and made his own chassis using Vitesse front suspension, Reliant back axle and an MG Magnette engine and gearbox. Several car projects later including kits, restorations and one-offs, he moved into marine and developed his GRP skills and then became intrigued with aviation and built two microlight aircrafts, one of which he flew to Madrid and back. His wife Elaine and daughter Charlotte were delighted when he gave up this potentially dangerous activity in favour of developing his own kit car business.

Stuart formed Mills Extreme Vehicles Ltd with fellow car enthusiast Julie Wilson and has since developed 26 various vehicles, most of which are available in kit form today. He has always been an advocate of the 'blinkers-off approach' and, whilst mostly self taught, he sees this as a testament that the education system that he bowed out of at 16 would have only slowed down his progress.

Acknowledgements

Many thanks to Julie Wilson for helping me write this book and to Jackie Cubitt for producing the illustrations. Thanks also to Adam at Performance Publishing and James at Panda Creative Ltd and most of all my Mum for having me!

Foreword

I HAVE AN excuse for writing this foreword and it's that I have been working alongside Stuart Mills for 30 years. This has been an absolute privilege and has also given me the opportunity to watch, learn and take part in the complete unflinching dedication and determination that is required to see a project through from a blank piece of paper to a finished vehicle and, sometimes, a best-selling car. The press occasionally report that British car manufacturing is dead. Actually, it's alive and well and thriving in garages and workshops near you, albeit sometimes on a small scale, or cottage industry as people like to call it. But it is there, and there is a mass of talent waiting to be brought to life. All they need is a bit of help, a bit of pointing in the right direction, arming with some knowledge, and a great big dollop of inspiration. That is what Stuart Mills is striving to provide by writing this book.

In business, people are often heard saying I am going to do this or I am going to do that, and nothing transpires. If Stuart releases a drawing or a teaser of a car saying this will be at the shows next year, then everyone knows it will be. Stuart has to date, designed, built and brought to market 26 vehicles. Some have been, and are, hugely commercially successful and others haven't. People who are closely involved with Mills Extreme Vehicles Ltd know that I joke about Monday mornings and Stuart arriving with an imaginary light bulb switched on over his head as he tells me "I've had an idea", and I listen with eager anticipation as he rolls out another innovation.

Stuart's approach is to come up with ideas for vehicles that he would personally like in his garage that are not available in the showrooms. It is interesting to hear his stories of when ideas have come to him, as sometimes it can be early morning, late at night, or sometimes even in the middle of the night. It is not unusual when we have locked up at 7pm and gone home for the evening, for Stuart to have been back at 10pm for a few hours saying to me the next morning "I didn't like it!", and a design has been altered! One editor even published in his magazine the headline "does the man never sleep?"!

Stuart's enormous appetite for creating cars and his intense attention to it throughout its gestation period is what has brought Mills Extreme Vehicles Ltd to the position it now occupies. MEV has a stable of cars which very possibly caters for almost everybody's different car-building desires; the electric power enthusiasts, the bike-engine trike enthusiasts, the bike-engine car enthusiasts, the exoskeletal enthusiasts, the semi-bodied enthusiasts, the full-bodied weather gear enthusiasts, the front-engine and mid-engine enthusiasts, and the classic retro enthusiasts.

As we sat one day contemplating his progress to date, Stuart pondered the idea that it may be considered a shame that he has all this experience, knowledge and enthusiasm and it's all hidden in a workshop in Mansfield, and so we came to discuss the possibility of a platform where Stuart could share all this, and a book was born.

The driving force behind this idea was to show others who may not have an idea how to begin any kind of car creating project, how to set about it and how to carry it through to fruition. The primary aim is to inspire and educate people how to make this happen. As we find ourselves in an era where people are engrossed in all things electronic, Stuart has found, through creating cars that are affordable, modern, and not too difficult to build, a whole new young generation of car builders. Some observers had thought this was not possible, and were watching our industry decline as the previous generation of enthusiastic builders aged. Bringing in these youngsters is what will keep home car building alive, and with this book comes the spark of inspiration that means these guys will take this baton and run with it.

You have only got to view the MEV Owners' Group forum to see that, while building a car supplied by us, new owners start to get ideas of their own. A natural progression of this is that they begin to innovate, and make changes. At first it is a way of customising their cars, or changing the way they approach certain aspects of their build. They compare this to the ways other builders are constructing and begin to have discussions on the forum about various aspects of their project, and the thought process starts to happen... inspiration.

This was one of the main reasons for Stuart's idea behind 'Build Guides' for our cars as opposed to 'instructions'. He steadfastly said he didn't want to tell people how to make every single bracket and every single mount. He said he wanted people to think about the build and come up with their own ideas, or discuss their ideas with others, and this is where technology has been invaluable. Through the internet these builders have got instant access to each other's builds and ways to communicate with each other that would previously have been thought impossible, and there is also another wave of people who have long discussed on internet forums various ways they would like to build a car or see a car built, but have never done it. I feel this book is a vehicle to encourage like-minded people to design and then build their own car. It may be a one-off, or it may be the basis for a whole new business, and this is the aim of this publication. Stuart can inspire people of all ages to design and build cars, and he knows that we can go a step further now, and encourage a new generation to pick up this book, read it, and go and create.

Jules Wilson
Co-Director
Mills Extreme Vehicles Ltd

Contents

Introduction

THE IDEA OF building a car, never mind the even more potentially daunting thought of actually designing one, would to most people seem outrageous and impossible. Surely that is something Ford or Mercedes do, and they're quite good at it so let's just leave it at that. On the other hand, let's not!

Everyone in the world, almost, has heard of Henry Ford, but before Ford produced millions of cars which are now scattered all over our planet with their instantly recognisable blue oval logo, Henry Ford was at one time an unknown chap with a bit of an idea to build a car, just like you. However we are not talking about you trying to become the next Henry Ford or trying to emulate any of the greats of the car industry. This is better than that. Design and build your own.

As a child you pushed little toy cars around the floor, then maybe progressed to a home-made go-cart, or a bought one if you were really lucky. After what may have seemed an age of waiting in eager anticipation, you finally got your driving licence and a car. Now go one wonderful leap further: design, build and drive your own car. Why settle for what a manufacturer thinks you should drive and is the same as the car lots of other people drive around in? We are talking about your own design, and the only thing that can stand in your way is you. Despite the fact that almost everyone you know drives a car, people are shocked at the idea of someone coming up with their own vehicle, and everyone will think you're stupendously clever to even be able to think of doing such a thing.

There are lots of what are termed 'kit car' building options, which come supplied to you in bits ready to marry up to some more bits from what is termed a 'donor' car, which is a production car from which you glean parts you need to complete the kit, such as the engine and transmission. This option is fine. However, the key word here is individuality, and when you're meeting friends and you tell someone you're building your own car, they may say "oh yeah a kit car, what make is it?" and you can proudly say "no, my own car, my design, my ideas. From a picture in my mind, into reality and onto the road, all mine." At this stage you can even say "it's called a ....". You fill in the blank.

Now that you have established that you can't go through life without having created your own road going work of art, let's put the 'pedal to the metal' and get on with it. Remember, as you work through this marvellous project, there are no problems, only solutions. If you hit a problem, it's only something you haven't yet found the answer to, there's no such thing as you can't, only that you may be experiencing a little difficulty. This is partly why doing a design and build is so much fun. You are in total control, you dictate the pace, and you will find yourself quite cosily absorbed in the whole process.

In this unique book you follow my thought, design and build processes. It will enable you to see at first hand the my decision-making in action, which gives you an insight into how I do it and giving you sufficient technical background to allow you to design and build your own car.

If you don't want to build a car but just want to learn how it's done, you will also enjoy this book as armchair or bath-time reading, and you will emerge equipped well enough to hold your own in conversations where any of the topics covered are raised. Enjoy the experience, whichever option you are choosing.

Stuart Mills
Co-Director
Mills Extreme Vehicles Ltd

Design Considerations

I ALWAYS START vehicle design concepts without fixed parameters. Daring to be different often results in all sorts of unconventional options being considered. Most modern cars are not a million miles away in design terms from the mode of transport they replace, namely the horse and cart, with the power up front, the driver behind and the passengers in the back. I try to create new designs that will have interesting contemporary body lines, beneath which lies an unusual but viable alternative to the often mundane offerings available.

Your approach here will be different to that of a major manufacturer. Where the likes of Ford designs its styling and engineers its mechanicals almost in unison, you will need to use what mechanical packages already exist. This means you will have to choose a suitable mechanical package and then create styling to suit. Of course, you'll be mindful of that styling goal while deciding on the underpinnings.

Budgetary constraints may limit what you are able to achieve and hamper your flair, and so the possibility of costs escalating must be considered from the outset. Designing a masterpiece and then finding yourself unable to fund its creation due to cost implications can be very frustrating. However, to ensure your design flow is not hampered you may wish to assume you have bottomless pockets and worry about funding later. If it is intended that your creation is to be put into production, funding may well be more flexible as it can be fine-tuned to match potential return from sales. I will cover amortising development cost, marketing and budgeting in Chapter 10 but right now let's get this thing started...

Beginning with a blank sheet of paper can often be a daunting prospect, so let us divide the designing process into bite size chunks. A design brief is therefore required. Nothing will be set in stone, however. Some compromise may be necessary as you proceed through the tasks ahead, but it may well be useful to look back throughout the process at the original brief that you set out for yourself, so that you don't drift too far from the mark. If you fail to keep within the envelope of your original brief then you may need to revisit the proposed use.

You'll need to consider all aspects of the vehicle as a whole, but generally I would tackle the job of setting a design brief in the following order:

1 Vehicle type: Is it going to be a single-seat track day car, a 4x4 off-roader or something in between?
2 Seating: You need to ensure there is enough space in the car for the occupants. Will it accommodate one, two or more people?
3 Mechanical package: Now is the time to consider front or rear-wheel drive, front or mid-engine, and an engine to suit the vehicle.
4 Styling: We come to this last to ensure your mechanical package fits within your bodywork, but the chances are you'll have an idea of the look of the car in your mind from the very start.

Initially you need to decide on use, to establish which type of vehicle you're going to design. Are you going to create an off-road vehicle with an aggressive stance on a four-wheel drive platform, or are you more interested in a lightweight bare-bones track day weapon? Somewhere near half-way between those two would be a roadster with good dynamics to have fun in on the country lanes. So once you have decided the initial application, let us then move on to a few obvious questions you must ask yourself, for instance how many seats? What type of engine/transmission? What will the finished vehicle look like? Are you going to design a centre-steer one-seat car, or make that three seats with a passenger either side of the driver?

OPTION 1: Front-engine front-wheel drive

Many modern production cars available today use this configuration. You will note that the compact package of a transverse engine and gearbox with integral differential is used to drive the front wheels. This results in more room for feet, no transmission tunnel, and can also mean that a lower floor may be possible. The rear suspension can be configured without the beam axle that is shown in the diagram here, which would allow for deeper luggage space.

For a family saloon this layout is ideal, but the downside is that front-wheel drive can introduce what is known as torque steer. This occurs when the engine torque has an effect on the steering, so during heavy acceleration the steering may pull to one side. It should also be considered that when a vehicle accelerates, the front tends to lift thus lessening the traction at the front. Conversely the back end may tuck in, suggesting that driving the rear wheels may lead to better traction during acceleration. Extreme driving, however, is not what a family saloon is intended for.

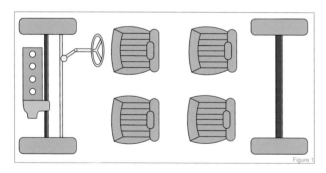
Figure 1

OPTION 2: Front-engine rear-wheel drive

Careful positioning of the main components can lead to a very well balanced car. The MEV Exocet, for instance, has a 50 per cent weight distribution front to rear when an 80kg driver is on board. Front engine, rear-wheel drive cars are often considered tail happy and liable to step out during corner exits, but in reality the MX-5 that the Exocet is based on is considered to be an exceptional handling car by many experts. However, not all cars of this type are particularly well balanced and can be light on the rear end, which can cause oversteer.

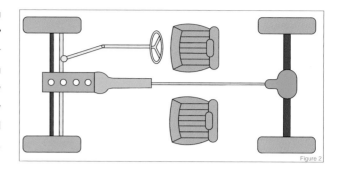
Figure 2

OPTION 3: Mid bike-engine rear-wheel drive

This layout was devised for the MEV Atomic in order to achieve the ultimate balanced performance car. With the average weight driver and carefully positioned engine, petrol tank and battery etc, it was possible to achieve a near perfect 25 per cent weight distribution to each corner. With the introduction of a very quick steering rack this vehicle has go-kart like characteristics and is an absolute hoot to drive.

It is unlikely to understeer (ie when a car steers less than intended by the driver due to the progressive loss of traction often induced by lack of weight over the steering wheels) or oversteer (ie when the rear end starts to step out often due to the lack of weight over the rear wheels). What happens with this vehicle on the limit is that the whole car tends to do a four-wheel drift when operated outside of its safe handling envelope.

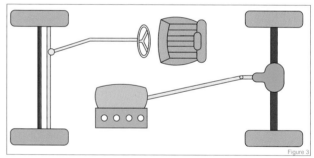
Figure 3

OPTION 4: Mid/rear four-cylinder transverse

Here you can see that the compact package from Fig 1 has been transferred to the rear wheels. The uprights for what are now the rear hubs would need replacing or the steering facility locking off.

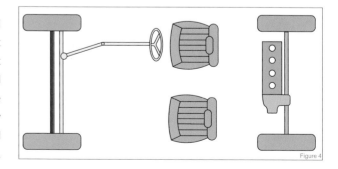
Figure 4

The result of this layout is excellent traction at the rear driven wheels which can be used well in racing with exceptional corner exit speeds.

However, in order to avoid understeer the driver must balance the car by using the polar moment of inertia (this is when weight is transferred from the rear to the front during braking) to ensure traction is maintained to the front wheels.

OPTION 5: Three-seat mid/rear V6 transverse

This is an interesting arrangement where the driver sits midships in a cab forward design (cab forward literally means the occupants sit further forward than normal, with the driver's feet close to the front axle line). Overlapping the two passenger seats with the driver's seat enables the shoulders of the occupants to overlap, thus enabling three seats to fit across a standard width car. In this case, I am showing a V6 transverse engine of the type taken from a Ford Mondeo, relocated to drive the rear wheels as per Fig 4.

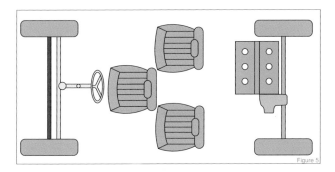

OPTION 6: Mid chain-drive bike engine

Here, I am showing a lightweight four-cylinder bike engine which is slightly offset from the centre line, enabling the drive sprocket to be mated to a chain sprocket that is bolted to the differential crown wheel. The modification of a standard differential in this manner is quite common, with the diff being removed from a standard casing and then lubricated with grease in sealed caps at each driveshaft.

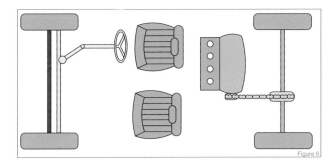

OPTION 7: Mid V8 inline

This may be a layout you are considering if the car you intend to design

is to be classed as a supercar. The V8 inline configuration using a transaxle can be classed as a true mid-engined car when compared to Figs 4 and 5, as it is clear the engine location in Fig 7 is nearer to the centre of the car to aid balance. The other advantage here is that a big V8 derivative is capable of producing massive amounts of power. Transaxles are available from several manufacturers who make bespoke units designed to mate to various V8 blocks, with gear set ratios to suit your application. This is not, however, the cheapest option by any means.

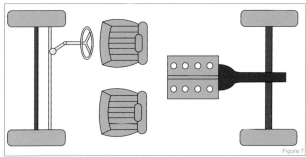

OPTION 8: Narrow body inline four-cylinder

Whilst very similar in configuration to the set-up in Fig 7, this inline four cylinder engine complete with transaxle could be of the type used by Audi to drive the front wheels. The advantages here are that this is a very straightforward transformation from front engined to mid-engine. In this particular example it is shown as a narrow body where the passenger's shoulders would overlap the driver's shoulders in order to keep the vehicle slim and aerodynamic.

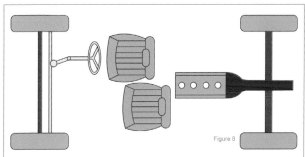

OPTION 9: Tandem seat, electric motor, 16 batteries

Here, you can see another way to create a narrow bodied aerodynamic vehicle, in this case with tandem seating. This would tend to increase the length of the cockpit space required, but here I am showing a vehicle driven by an electric motor which is far more compact than an internal combustion engine. It is shown driving the rear axle via either a bespoke transfer box or a chain drive to a modified diff as per Fig 6. There is also an indication that it may well be possible to mount 16 batteries within the given space. Of course,

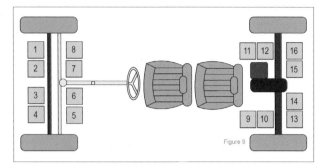

Figure 9

if you go down this route you will be overjoyed when the lady behind the glass at the Post Office hands you a free tax disc.

OPTION 10: Front engine four or eight-cylinder 4x4

Here I am showing a conventional layout of a Suzuki or Land Rover 4x4. Both vehicles are designed around a ladderframe type chassis (see chassis design chapter). The advantage here is that, if you use one of those cars as a basis, once the unwanted body is removed, the drivetrain and suspension remain as a rolling chassis ensuring conversion to your design is relatively straightforward, and provided the chassis is not modified in any way it will not be required to go through the UK registration process.

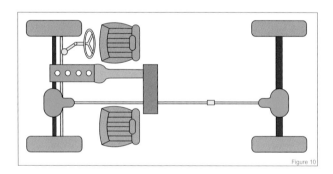

Figure 10

OPTION 11: Rear engine with inverted beam axles

Here, I have taken the major components as per Fig 10 and re-arranged them to create a mid engine configuration. When looking down on plan view, you can see that the engine has rotated through 180deg, and it was therefore necessary to rotate the axles upside down to reverse the rotation of the drive system.

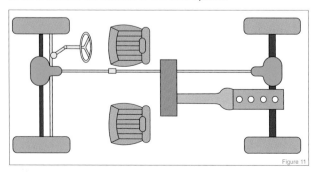

Figure 11

OPTION 12: Hybrid petrol electric

The front engine set up is the same as Fig 1, but to the rear I am showing two electric motors which can drive via chains or gearboxes independently to the back wheels.

The advantage with this arrangement is that a differential will not be required, and instead the motor controller will be configured to favour torque loadings which will enable one wheel to rotate faster than the other in a corner. Also shown is space for the provision of 12 batteries which could be used if the connections are paralleled as a 12-volt system or if in series, 144-volt system, or in two banks of six for a 72-volt system, known as series/parallel.

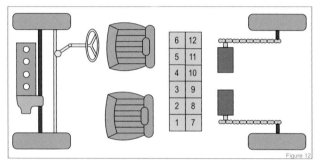

Figure 12

OPTION 13: Three-wheelers

One option we have not covered in detail is the possibility of fewer wheels – a trike. Hold that thought if the idea floats your boat. We will briefly cover trikes in Chapter 4.

One of the above will no doubt suit your design but on the other hand you may have now been given inspiration to come up with your own layout or a combination of any of the above. You must consider at this stage what is available for you to use. It can be cost prohibitive to come up with a mechanical layout that would need specialist engineering so let's also look at what is commonly available.

Once the mechanical and seating layout has been determined, it would be helpful to draw a simple sketch, having taken measurements to determine your requirement for elbow room and leg room. Your initial sketch, however, will only need a measurement from the front bulkhead to the back of the seats and an internal width, you have then determined the cockpit space requirement. Later, the sketch will develop into a scale drawing from which to base your final design.

However, prior to that stage we must consider the powerplant and drivetrain. Are you intending to use a motorcycle engine with a chain drive to a modified differential? Will it be an in line (north-south) V6? Or a transverse (east-west) four-cylinder engine? Are you looking at petrol power, or diesel? Do you desire to install a four-wheel drive system with front and rear differentials and a central transfer box? Or are you considering powering your new vehicle with an electric motor, in which case you would need to calculate the battery capacity required in order to ensure that your vehicle has room to accommodate the same.

You need to consider the output power required and to gain an idea of performance you will need to hazard a guess at the all-up weight of your complete vehicle.

As a rough guide, a lightweight motorcycle powered two-seater can be around 400kg, whereas some of the heavier large production cars are around 2000kg. The power to weight ratio is the important factor here, and there are online calculators which will give you a rough guide to 0-60mph times once you enter torque characteristics and all up weight of a given example.

For instance, a normally aspirated (not turbo or supercharged) 1.6-litre engine will produce roughly 100bhp. If taken from an average five door family saloon that weighs say 1400kg, the performance increase will be huge once installed in a lightweight sports car. So if your car weighs 500kg that 100bhp equates to 200bhp per tonne (in the 1400kg saloon it equated to just 71bhp per tonne). The weight of the vehicle will vary enormously depending upon powerplant and body style. A V8 four-wheel drive system, for instance, can easily weigh 200kg more than a bike engined derivative. Before making a decision on which engine/fuel type, we must consider the required torque characteristics. A 1000cc bike engine will produce relatively low torque figures, achieving maximum power through high revs. Diesel inline five-cylinder engines produce relatively high torque figures at low rpm, whereas a more common four-cylinder petrol engine will produce its peak torque at easily accessible rpm.

It is important, therefore, to consider the application, and a simple explanation is to consider torque as being the rotational force available and bhp being the speed at which the torque can be applied. A heavy vehicle, or one that is used to move heavy loads, will require more torque or lower gearing than a lightweight vehicle, hence a 1000cc screamer may well be considered suitable for a lightweight track day car, but a vehicle intended to tow a two-ton trailer would be more at home with a low revving petrol V8, or a diesel engine.

Whatever type of vehicle you desire, it should be considered that more torque would be desirable if you add doors, a windscreen and roof, as these will also severely increase the weight and therefore lower the performance. If you want to make life easier for yourself, it has to be considered that the introduction of doors, that are both air and watertight with locks, hinges and wind up windows, are going to severely hamper the design process. Of course, a fully enclosed car is far more practical than a bare bones racer. It should be noted however that the vast majority of low volume car manufacturers avoid doors, roofs and windscreens. I think I know why!

As part of your basic brief, you should also consider the layout, primarily due to the fact that if the vehicle you are designing is to be streamlined and aerodynamic, then this desired external appearance is far easier to achieve with a rear mounted powerplant. There are ways around everything, though. For instance, front engine production cars such as those from Aston Martin seem to belie the fact that a huge V8 or V12 sits up front, but their later cars have a dry sump, enabling them to fit the powerplant lower, and a V engine is generally lower than a four-cylinder with upright pistons.

Transverse engines are used by most manufacturers. The Ford Focus (see Fig 1) for instance uses a front engine transverse

■ *If you take a 1.6-litre engine from a family car weighing about 1400kg, its performance will increase hugely in a lightweight car.*

■ *The motor and batteries fitted to the Missile, a MEV model which was offered only in electric powered form.*

■ *If you want to create a streamlined car, a mid-engined layout helps with a low frontal area. MEV R2 also featured staggered seating.*

arrangement driving the front wheels. But then if you consider taking this powerplant and fitting it in the rear of your car the only thing you need change is the fact that the car will steer from the rear, which is not considered a desirable option, so you will need to lock off the steering or, to do the job properly, you will need to design a replacement upright with track adjustment (see Fig 4).

Some Renaults use an inline front engine mated to a gearbox that drives the front wheels. This unit, which is known as a transaxle, could be very useful if transferred to the rear, resulting in the engine being ahead of the rear axle, thus assisting weight distribution (see Fig 8). An interesting layout that utilised the Renault V6 engine and transaxle was used by De Lorean. It was not considered the best configuration, as the engine was located aft of the rear axle line causing weight distribution issues. It was also necessary for the

■ *The Mazda MX-5 is a good base for a sports car build. The entire engine, drivetrain and suspension are used in full for several MEVs.*

crown wheel and pinion set to be flipped over in order to gain forward drive in forward gears.

Mazda MX-5s and RX-7s/8s use a front mounted engine driving the rear wheels, as do BMW and Aston Martin. This is often considered to be the traditional British racing car layout (see Fig 2). The MX-5's dynamics are seldom criticised.

The entire drivetrain including engine, gearbox, propshaft, differential, and the subframes (including suspension) to which these components are mounted in the Mazda MX-5 as shown in the photo. This set-up as pictured from the MX-5 is used to build the MEV Exocet, Mevster and Replicar.

The latter, however, would benefit from the installation of a straight six engine as per the original Aston Martin DBR1, but this can easily be achieved by modifying the front subframe engine mounts whilst still retaining the superb dynamics of the MX-5.

Motorcycle engines are an interesting choice and can be mated to specialist differentials via a chain (see Fig 6), or if turned through 90deg (see Fig 3) they can be mated directly to a standard differential at the rear wheels via a propshaft and a propshaft adaptor, which replaces the gearbox output chain sprocket. This is how MEV configured the Atomic.

Big V8 engines are a popular choice amongst specialist vehicle designers. These engines are often sourced from luxury cars but can be hampered by an automatic gearbox, unless that is desired of course. Adaptor plates are available to mate these engines to a variety of manual gearboxes and some use a Porsche transaxle that is turned upside down and finishes up behind the engine (Fig 7). When fitted to a Porsche, they have the engine on what is often considered the 'wrong' side of the axle line, thus compromising the car's balance. Porsche, however, compensated for this with a complex

■ *Motorcycle engines are popular in lightweight sports cars, and can be used with chain drive, as shown on this MK Midi.*

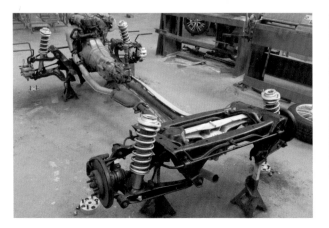

■ *Always explore unconventional ideas. MEV Trek used the drivetrain from a four-wheel drive Land Rover, but with the engine in the rear.*

and very well developed rear suspension arrangement – oh, and of course much wider rear tyres than fitted on the front.

Having looked at the options, we must consider the amount of torque we are about to apply to the chosen gearbox. It is generally not considered a clever option to feed 200ft lb through a gearbox

■ *The electric MEV Missile had only 11kW, but was capable of 50mph thanks to its low weight.*

from, say, a Ford Ka. It may not last long but then if your car is considerably lighter it may not be an issue when you consider that torque can only be applied given sufficient traction. However, a tuned V8 may well eat Porsche transaxles.

Possibilities become far more interesting when you remove your blinkers and start getting creative. I never accept the word 'no' as an answer when considering the options. You should try questioning every element of a car's design, and try to work out what was in the designer's mind when looking in-depth into conventional existing products. One example of thinking outside the box is a MEV Trek. Here I used the drivetrain from a four-wheel drive Land Rover (see Fig 10) but fitted the V8 in the rear (see Fig 11). The result would have been a car that went very fast backwards but only had one forward gear. But by mounting the axles upside down the drive was reversed so it finished up with just one reverse gear! You can see from Fig 10 that the off-centre differentials have changed position as they have been rotated through 180deg in Fig 11.

There are other options. Electric is one (Fig 9). A motor from a fork lift truck driving a chain to a diff or as is often done, an electric motor adapted to drive a gearbox, but of course as the motors can produce maximum torque from zero rpm there is little point in changing gear.

Hybrids could be an interesting option, too. Imagine a front-mounted engine driving the front wheels in a conventional manner

■ *Not all hybrids have to be like the Toyota Prius! Imagine your car with an electric motor driving the front wheels and an engine out back.*

whilst at the rear an electric motor can be engaged to drive the rear wheels. That could be very useful as you have a 4x4 if both drives are used simultaneously, both aiding traction and power output (Fig 12).

Here the layout needs careful consideration as batteries can be very bulky. Firstly you need to decide on the power output required from the motor. A good starting point is the MEV Missile, which has only 11kW (kilo watts) but is capable of 50mph due to its light weight. The motor drives the rear wheels via a directly connected differential and the 18 batteries are distributed around the car to aid balance and basically to find the space needed. The batteries are 60ah (amp hours) each which when multiplied by the total voltage of 216 gives an output capacity of 13kW/h. This pack should therefore be able to drive a 13kW motor at full power for one hour. In reality the losses and high current levels reduce this figure to nearer half that. The motor however is not using full power unless it is accelerating or pulling the vehicle up hill so the result is a range of up to one hour at 50mph. These figures are a good starting point for anyone considering an EV but it should be noted that by digging deeper into my pockets and using Lithium batteries then the range could easily be doubled over the output obtainable from our lead acid traction batteries.

If you fancy going down the four-wheel drive route with a conventional combustion engine then remember that the required components are collectively quite bulky. There are three differentials required as both axles need a diff together with a centre diff in the transfer case to stop what is known as transmission wind up (front axle rotating faster than the rear).

Finding room for a centre transfer case and two propshafts can result in the floor height being above your desired level – seating may need to be high, thus the height of the body increases. It is possible to keep these units compact. Ford made a 4x4 Sierra which

was not obviously a 4x4 from the outside. If you can find one it could be the bones of a very interesting vehicle.

One other point to consider is that an open-topped car with doors will compromise the structural integrity of the chassis. It is far easier to design a stiff chassis if rails are introduced at shoulder height. However, a car with a door and a roof has effectively put a lid on an open box.

For a moment, if you just imagine an open cardboard box, twisting the box requires little effort, but a closed box becomes considerably stiffer. A stiff roll cage can often be bolted in to compensate for what would otherwise be considered a poor chassis design. That said, if you intend to create a macho off-roader then it may be considered appropriate to have an aggressive appearance with a large front grille featured relatively high off the ground.

The next stage of an evolutionary car design process will be to first consider what you intend your car design to look like. I will assume at this point that you have a picture in your mind and that there are comparables already gracing our roads. You must ask yourself in what way your own design is superior to what is already available.

Will it be lighter, more powerful, more aerodynamic, or are you introducing a feature or features into your vehicle that are not available in the main dealer showrooms? Starting off with a comparable car is always going to be helpful. There is no point in trying to re-invent the wheel if there is something out there that in some ways is similar to allow you to take even the most rudimentary measurements from. This or these comparable vehicles will also serve as a benchmark as your design progresses. I have mentioned seating and engine choices etc, so now let us consider the proposed layout in more detail to enable you to complete and finalise your brief.

YOUR FINAL BRIEF

Body style: Sports, race, commuter, off-roader, or camper van etc.
Seating arrangements: Be it one, two, three, four, and layout.
Mechanical layout: Front or rear engine etc.
Styling: The vehicle's appearance.

Throughout the whole of this process, it is important to keep a visual in your mind of your intended finished product. If you were to ask a songwriter if they write the music or the lyrics first, it would be often difficult to get a straight answer. Likewise with a car, if you design the body first there may be serious compromise required when it comes to accommodating the mechanical package. On the other hand, finalising the seating and engine configuration without due consideration to the vehicle's external appearance may well also cause

■ *Does your new design offer something that can't be found elsewhere? Does it set any new benchmarks?*

problems. So the balancing act required is to keep in mind your intended body style whilst looking at the various alternative layouts discussed in this chapter. For example, your car won't look like a Lamborghini if you try and house a Rover V8 in the front.

At the start of this chapter, I suggested you consider drawing a sketch. Moving on from this you can refine your sketch or sketches to produce a scale drawing, only as a guide at this stage but the more accurate you can be the more chance there is of the package working at a later stage.

To start this process, you need to either switch on your PC and select a suitable software programme, such as Google SketchUp or Adobe Illustrator if you are competent or, alternatively, get some graph paper, a scale rule, protractor, pencils and, most importantly, an eraser! If you are not already experienced at using software for drawing, it must be pointed out that this is a whole new skill set and I do not consider it essential as it can result in a considerable amount of extra time being spent when compared to a simple pencil sketch.

Once you're sitting comfortably and in the correct frame of mind, without the television on in the background, the dog barking, or someone looking over your shoulder, it is time to put pen to paper

or finger to mouse. You can start by simply choosing a layout from Figs 1 to 12, or devise a combination of two or more of the same. It could be useful to scan or photocopy your chosen layout, so that once you have decided on the basic dimensions these can be applied to the illustrations as a reference point for your scale drawing. A word of warning: don't use a Biro unless you have a considerable amount of correction fluid available!

It may be helpful to consider the one, two or three-box approach, which can be very useful as a starting point if you are not too skilled in this area. The idea being that your finished car will 'fit' in the box or boxes so you will get a good idea of proportions. You can use one box for a van or people mover design. A one-box approach with a lower top would also be applicable for a screenless, roofless roadster. Two boxes will enable you to fit a hatchback style car, an off road type, or small van in, and three boxes would be ideal if you plan to have a roof, a bonnet, and a boot.

These basic box sketches will enable you to build the picture, check dimensions, and ensure you, your passengers and your chosen power plant will fit.

It's helpful to measure existing cars to get a feel for the proportions and space required. You should compare the steering wheel and pedal positions, and seat heights, from a saloon to a sports car, or a van to a 4x4 in order to determine your seat position and confirm the cockpit space requirement of your initial sketch, assuming you did as suggested early in this chapter. It is recommended that you take accurate measurements of the engine, transmission etc. It may be helpful to start with something along these lines when we move on to the body design later in the book. Bear in mind that in order to help visualise a car within the box or boxes it may help if you 'lean' the windscreen section or rear end.

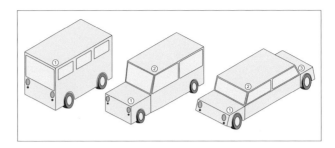

■ *You can start with the most basic shapes before tweaking your design to look as you intend the finished item to appear.*

Now you can scale these measurements on to your drawing and refine accordingly. Once you're happy remember they are not etched in stone and may need altering later but you will at least have passed the blank sheet of paper stage. Of course, it's better to make mistakes on paper or computer than in reality.

Now to test your calculations and desired design it may prove very useful to make a mock-up. This can be done on a very rudimentary

■ *As your design progresses, your sketches should become more accurate. You could use a package like Google SketchUp.*

level by using a block of wood to sit on and cardboard boxes to surround you whilst you check your measurements. Alternatively, you could make a timber frame. It's far easier to change this mock up than a steel frame at a later date, and the mock-up will give you an idea of proportion and hopefully inspire confidence in your ability. This can be a very exciting stage of the process. No doubt you will not be able to resist making brum brum noises!

There are three ways in which you may be able to protect your design, invention and trademark, which we come to in Chapter 13.

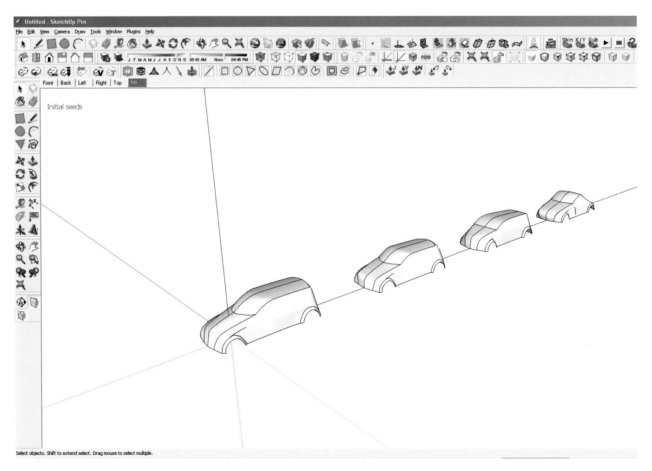

2 Required Skills and Tools

PEOPLE MAY ASSUME there is a requirement to possess qualifications of some sort to undertake the entire design and build of a vehicle from start to finish. They would be wrong, and I am the proof (26 times over!). The most important skills (or traits) are enthusiasm, a willingness to learn as you go along, and a strong desire to see the project through to its end. I only achieved a Grade 2 in CSE woodwork (the exam of that time!) when I left school. There are no letters after my name and I strongly believe that I attended the best University in the world, the University of Life. Here I learned so much that could not be taught through text books. No form of learning beats practical experience, jumping in and getting your hands dirty and finding out for yourself how things go together (or come apart!).

Give it a try and you'll amaze yourself by what you can achieve. This approach can sometimes be frustrating if you can't work out a problem, but more often than not you will be able to find a workshop manual or a friendly search engine to provide an answer. Learning by making mistakes is no fun so, wherever possible, I prefer to see if I can find information on the subject, where someone before has made mistakes that I can learn from. These days finding that information is so easy – just click your mouse and you can save many hours. A word of caution, though: be careful, there's lots of rubbish on the worldwide web!

FABRICATION SKILLS
Your chassis (and, possibly, wishbones depending on which car you choose for your underpinnings) will need to be fabricated. If this is your first attempt at designing and building a car, there may be some stages where you might need to enlist professional help depending on your level of skill and how involved you want to become. The most cost-efficient way to fabricate a chassis is to use a MIG welder

■ *If you're going to weld your own chassis, you need to be proficient.*

■ *MIG welding is easier and more affordable than TIG welding. Enlist a professional to build the chassis if necessary.*

■ *An alternative to a steel spaceframe chassis is a monocoque. This requires a different set of skills.*

(metal inert gas). Sometimes TIG welders (tungsten inert gas) are used. This is a more costly and time-consuming process, as it's harder to learn and the equipment is more expensive. If you are an experienced welder, well and good. If not, you should get an experienced welder to do this for you. You don't want to be heading down a track one day and find your chassis trying to go in two different directions!

One of your alternatives is to work from your design and fabricate a chassis by tacking the joints together and then asking a skilled welder to seam all of your joints. Another option is to attend evening classes at your local technical college. Some colleges run a 12-week introduction to welding (beginners) course. There is no qualification at the end but it's an excellent way of getting an understanding of the processes involved in welding, grasping the basics and getting lots of practice. If you really enjoy it you can progress to a more involved course that will give you a qualification at the end. Always

■ *Sheet metalwork is a skill you'll require early on in assembly. Spaceframe chassis are typically skinned with aluminium.*

get any welding you have done checked by a competent experienced welder. If you prefer not to do the welding, once you have worked out your chassis dimensions, you can get a local metal fabricator to cut and weld your chassis for you. If you do build your own chassis, it's important you have considerable experience of welding before you drive a chassis you've fabricated. The downside of outsourcing is having to be very specific in your instructions – you lose the 'make it up as you go along' option.

If you are going to fabricate a monocoque from aluminium sheet, folders and a guillotine are required but, again, you can enlist the help of local firms to do this for you if required. You may well need to consider making a jig or jigs to hold sections of your chassis in place during the fabrication process. I will go into the details of the considerations and methods for designing and making your chassis in the Chapter 4, Chassis Design.

SHEET METALWORK SKILLS

Sheet metalwork can often form a large part of the fabrication of a low volume or one-off car. Often used as stress plates (diaphragms) to strengthen chassis sections where steel or aluminium sheet is riveted or screwed to the chassis.

Thin aluminium such as 1.2mm, previously knows as 18swg, is often used to form interior panels, inner wheelarches, and covers for the transmission tunnel or bulkheads. It is possible to carry out this sheet metalwork without the use of a guillotine or folder (also known as a press brake). A standard jig saw with a fine tooth blade can be used to cut the metal, and clamping metal between two lengths of 50mm by 50mm timber or angle iron can allow you to create a fold. Skills in this area are relatively easy to learn. Working with stiff cardboard to experiment is a good way to gain experience at a low cost. It is only like

wallpapering your hall, stairs and landing, but using sheet metal instead, cutting into corners and making folds is more a matter of practise to develop the skill, rather than something that can easily be taught.

MECHANICAL SKILLS INCLUDING VEHICLE ELECTRICS

People would assume that a good grasp of mechanical knowledge would be needed to set about such a project. However, a significant number of MEV kits have been built by people who have never

■ *If you're retaining a donor loom, label it thoroughly on removal. Un-needed plugs may look very important when it comes to fitting.*

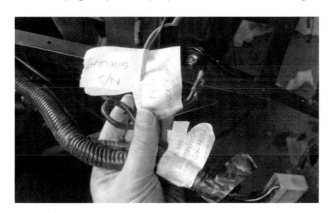

■ *A methodical approach to stripping your base car will pay dividends later on. You don't need to be a mechanic to build a car.*

previously picked up a spanner. The same principle applies to building a car of your own design. A methodical approach will pay enormous dividends. If you begin stripping a car which you are using as a base for your new car then make sure you are tidy. Label items and place them in boxes where you can find them later, and make sure you label every bit of the engine wiring loom as you dismantle it. Unsurprisingly, vehicle wiring is often the area that people are most scared of, but it can be frustrating more than anything else. Patience and a methodical way of working through always finds the problem. When you remove a wiring loom from a production car and then re-locate it into your car there will be a host of items you will not require, such as connections for the electric windows, the heated seats, the motors for the pop-up headlights, etc. So labelling is important, as it can be quite daunting looking at a plug on your car with no label when actually you felt at the time of dismantling that a label was not required on say, the speaker plug, as you were not transferring the radio. However, with no label, that plug looks as though it could be mighty important.

Some items you remove will make the ECU think something is wrong and your car will refuse to start. The most common

■ *If it all worked before stripping, it should work when reassembled – even if you're not sure what everything is!*

explanation for this is an earth which has been left off. To give you an example, when we build the MEV Exocet, there are no fewer than seven earths which need to be re-connected! And almost everybody forgets to put them all on at the first attempt. It is just a question of going back over your tracks, and carefully going through your steps until the reason it won't start jumps out at you. One of the most satisfying moments you will experience in the build is when it fires up for the first time.

■ *Advanced drawing skills are not vital, but it is useful to get your ideas down on paper for reference.*

Becoming an expert mechanic or qualified auto electrician is not necessary though, provided you choose to remove components from a car that was in full working order before you started pulling it apart. There is no reason for any parts you remove to become faulty once they are re-located.

In theory then, you are not repairing anything as all you are actually doing is transplanting components from one vehicle to another, and sometimes it's not even necessary to understand what the parts are, but if a part is plugged into an engine wiring harness you better transfer it across to be on the safe side.

DRAWING SKILLS

In Chapter 1, I discussed sketches and drawings. It is absolutely not necessary to possess any advanced drawing skills. Of course your renderings will look nicer if you are good at this, but there are so many avenues open to us now to get our rough sketches into a presentable looking piece of art that you don't need to worry about this. There are ranks of firms offering computer graphic services that can take a rough sketch and present you with a work of art.

What will be more important when you reach this stage is that you don't allow anyone to start utilising any artistic licence by altering parts of your design. Make sure you get what is in your mind and in your sketch. You don't have to draw the design, you could just form it physically. But it's easier to have something to refer to as you work.

When you get to this stage, your chassis and layout will have been designed and you will understand that changes to any one area or part of your car could severely jeopardise the chances of it fitting your chassis or body design without alteration to one or the other. I call it the Rule of Nine, change one thing and it may backfire down the line causing you to change nine others.

■ *Making a pattern from which the body moulds are taken is a thoroughly creative process. You can revise it as much as necessary.*

■ *Once you've made your pattern, a mould will be taken from it in order to make a series of GRP panels.*

PATTERN MAKING SKILLS

This is where my woodwork CSE qualification comes into use! In order to obtain a finished GRP item (or part of your bodywork), there has to be a mould. The mould is taken from a pattern which is essentially a mould from which the production plug is taken. There are numerous ways to set about this. A pattern can be made by using a series of templates, usually plywood, which when put together form a car shaped egg box. Filling in the gaps of this honeycomb structure

with expanding foam from an aerosol can or off-cuts of polyurethane foam will create the shape you require.

A copious amount of filler is used which is then sanded to get a smooth and even surface. Polyurethane is much easier to shape than car body filler but will not create a surface smooth enough for a mould to be taken. So in a nutshell, pattern making skills will involve the use of traditional woodworking materials and tools, but will also include the use of materials such as car body filler to achieve the required finish. The woodworker skills will also overlap into what could be described as a process used by sculptors. This can be considered a difficult role to fulfill, but it is a skill that develops the further into the task you find yourself. Getting it wrong is actually not a major issue; sand off too much foam or filler and you just need to stick some more back on.

I sometimes make templates as described above for certain patterns, but it can be tremendously time-consuming and I find I can make the shapes by using the fabricated chassis as a base to work from, and using plywood, MDF, flexi ply (5mm thick with the grain for each layer all running in the same direction), jelutong (low density hardwood), tacks, screws, wood glue and filler. This is also time-

■ *GRP is light and easy to manage, especially if your car is made from several panels. Gelcoat means no painting is required.*

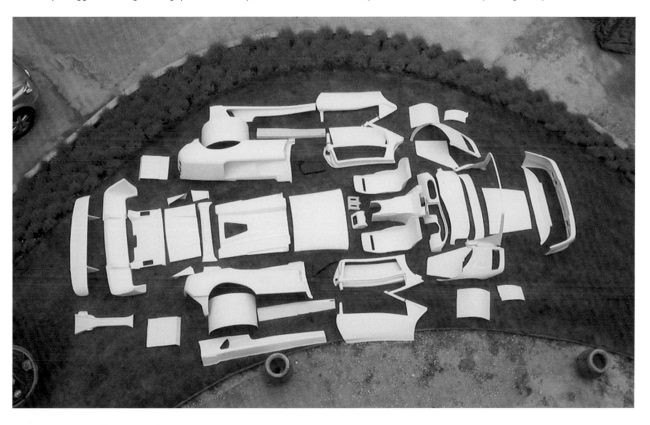

■ *Working with GRP allows you to make complex curved shapes which would be possible with the pressed steel used by mainstream cars.*

■ *You could choose to form panels from aluminium. For a production run, this would be time-consuming and costly.*

consuming but it gives me a little more scope to make changes as I go along if I want to.

GLASS REINFORCED PLASTIC AND CARBONFIBRE LAMINATING SKILLS

Production car bodies are almost always made from steel. There are many reasons why specialist car makers don't use steel, not least the fact that it requires huge tooling investment and confines the specialist car builder to parameters he would not want to be controlled by. There's a limit to the complexity of the shapes that can be created in steel. GRP, commonly known as fibreglass, is the material I have utilised for all the bodies on my car designs so far. It is a wonderful material that's so versatile we can make curves and sleek lines on car bodies without joins that would be required for a pressed steel version.

The finished product, especially if your car is made up of a number of different body panels, is light and easy to manage and it can be impregnated with a gelcoat in the colour of your choice giving us a highly polished unblemished finish. If you need to alter the shape later it's not difficult to alter the mould. The skills involved to work with GRP could again be considered as a cross between wallpapering and jelly making.

You will need to learn how to wax a mould, or apply a release agent, and then how to mix the gelcoats and resins before applying the chopped strand mat. Professional laminators use rollers to apply resin to the mat and to ensure that all air pockets are removed. I have to say this is not my favourite task and quite often in the past I have found myself producing a wooden pattern to a reasonably high standard, and then sending it to a body shop to be painted before getting my laminator to produce a GRP mould from it. It is sticky stuff, it seems to get everywhere, you tend to get splinters and the dust and

smell you have to put up with are not everyone's idea of fun.

That said, it is very rewarding to split a mould and pull out the final piece that you have been working towards. I would definitely encourage people to try their hand at the GRP game, if only to produce a relatively small item such as a petrol flap cover or instrument binnacle. If you get it wrong you will not have wasted much money but you will at least have come to appreciate why laminators charge what appear to be high fees for small items. It can actually take two or three days for one man to build up enough wax on a car body before he even starts taking a mould.

Short cuts in this area usually turn into disasters – especially if you find your cast will not release and you finish up destroying it and damaging the mould in an attempt to get a peep at what you have created. Most kit car manufacturers outsource the laminating of GRP panels.

Another option is to form body panels from aluminium. This is considerably more costly in terms of the time it takes and the skills required. If you're building a one-off, don't rule it out.

SENSE, LOGIC AND HEALTH AND SAFETY SKILLS

You must ensure that you are aware of health and safety issues from the beginning. Take your time and give some proper thought to each task as you approach it, think about the consequence of an action – ie what will happen if I release that jubilee clip? Is that pipe under pressure?

If you are concerned, make further investigations before proceeding. I would recommend that prior to actually doing any manual work you carry out your own risk assessment. Make sure that your working environment is as safe as you can make it for yourself and anyone else who happens to be around either helping you or observing. This will particularly apply to the stripping down of any donor vehicles you undertake, as you contend with items such as

■ *Personal protective equipment is the name given to safetywear. Ensure you have the right gear and that you're using it correctly.*

airbags and air conditioning units. Take all the steps you can to ensure you do not put yourself or anyone else at risk. The same applies when working underneath vehicles. Never rely on a jack, always use axle stands in addition. Always remove watches, rings and any other jewellery before working on a vehicle and, if your hair is long, ensure that you tie it back. All this will help you to avoid mishaps.

Hopefully the prerequisite skills for the health and safety area do not require you to turn into a first aider and apply too many sticking plasters. The skill here is actually knowing what could be dangerous and cause injury, and also that of using the right equipment known as personal protective equipment (PPE). Research this subject and put your mind at rest. Over the years I have had to visit the eye hospital and have bits of metal removed even though I always wear safety

glasses. As a tip, remember to make sure that these fit closely to your face as metal can bounce off your cheek and into your eye. Another tip is to watch out for restricted vision, as the safety glasses steam up when you wear a dust mask. I suggest you always wear a dust mask when required but it may be useful to get a can of moisture repellent spray that motorcyclists use. Otherwise you may find yourself protecting your lungs with a mask, and your eyes with goggles, but the combination of the two causes you to hurt your fingers.

MARKETING SKILLS

Chapter 10 covers marketing, funding and budgeting in more detail. It may be worth considering that although any salesman would argue in defence of his acquired skills, I believe that marketing, just like many other tasks in this book, is something that virtually anyone can learn given common sense, a reasonable approach, a level head and no personality disorder.

If you are making a one-off car for yourself then ignore this section, but if you are contemplating building a vehicle with the intention of putting it into low batch production or selling it on for someone else to do the same, then a certain level of marketing skill will need to be developed, unless you are experienced in this field. It could be argued that if the product is right and the price is right then it will sell itself, but it's not quite that simple. Marketing requires initiative, and your product will need to be offered to the right audience if it is going to succeed. Marketing skills include designing or coming up with ideas for adverts, getting your vehicles under the public's noses by choosing the right shows, the right online forums, and ensuring that you have a good website which is fine-tuned for search engine optimisation.

■ *A good quality website and well presented sales literature are must-haves in order to project the right image.*

■ *Your sales technique at shows needn't be pushy – people will choose to buy your car if it fits the market's needs at the right price.*

■ *Some tools are vital from the start, others can be bought as and when required. Just ensure you have the essentials to begin the project.*

Marketing is not about a pushy salesman who could sell ice to Eskimos or coal to Newcastle, it's more about giving potential customers confidence by portraying the right image, offering a good back-up service and building up a good reputation. I have been accused in the past of producing leaflets and having a website which don't give the right impression – using the excuse "we sell cars not websites" will not help. The general rule is that a quality website gives the impression of a quality product. Every element of your business acumen will be needed if you are to succeed and hiring in professionals to carry out the marketing for you is probably going to be cost prohibitive.

My opinion is that there is nothing to worry about here, but it is likely that when you meet a potential customer you will be so enthusiastic about your product that they should at least start to feel confident that you will get it right. If you haven't got the necessary skills or confidence to enable you to close a deal, the chances are that they will offer you a payment as they will be sold on your product and apparent commitment.

TOOLS REQUIRED

A tool kit is required to get on with any kind of work – ie stripping

items you want from a production car. Unless you are already equipped with these, you need to go shopping. My tip is not to go and buy a plethora of items you may never need. Basic essentials are as follows:

Socket and ratchet set	Spanners
Crow bar	Hammer
Screwdrivers	Steel drill bits
Metal punch	Bench vice
Set square	Steel ruler
Rivet gun	Pillar drill
Sheet metal cutters	Tape measure
Angle grinder	Files
Engine hoist (can be hired)	Safety glasses
Jig saw	Ear protection
Hack saw	Gloves
Axle stands	Dust masks
Trolley jack	Electric drill
G-clamps	Bench grinder

If you want to make your life a little easier, a small compressor and an air powered rivet gun will really make you happy later, and of course you can use the compressor for a multitude of other tasks such as blowing dust away and inflating tyres. Beyond this list, I would suggest you purchase other items only as and when you need them.

It is advisable not to let the design be dictated by the tools you think are available. If you want to design a chassis with bent tubes rather than straight lines everywhere it is possible, even though you may not have the expensive machinery capable of doing this. Local firms will be available who have CAD operated tube bending facilities (known as tube manipulators), and they make easy work of producing your desired curves or bends from a straight piece of tube. If you do not want to go to the expense of CAD operated tube bending, you could get someone to bend the tubes on a draw bender, which is self-explanatory as it draws the tube through the machine to a fixed radius, or a ring roller where the tube is fed through the rollers to produce a slow curve.

The same can be said for laser-cutting services. You may need to design brackets for some areas of your car which you may not be able to fabricate yourself. You may want to have them laser profile cut. This makes for a really professional job, and all you have to do

is give the firm a drawing of what you require with the measurements on. Don't worry if you cannot produce a CAD drawing, I used to turn up with something scribbled on the back of a cigarette packet if I was in a rush, as the laser cut firms tend to have their own CAD operators.

MACHINERY AVAILABLE

CAD operated tube bender	**Draw bender**
Box and pan folder	**Engine hoist (can be hired)**
Ring roller	**Brake press/folder**
MIG/TIG welder	**Circular steel cutting saw**
Guillotine	**Lathe**
Milling machine	**Band saw**

■ *Make the most of outsourcing for a professional finish. For example, you won't need to invest in expensive tube-bending machinery yourself.*

■ *This is a CAD drawing, as opposed to a CAD rendering. You can get away with giving laser cutting firms rough hand-drawn sketches.*

3 Sourcing Parts

THE CHASSIS AND body of your car are your own exclusive design and the cost involved in producing them is dictated largely by you. Budgeting of this will be covered later in the book. However, there are parts required for your car which can be extremely expensive if you purchase new without first researching. The engine alone could possibly run into thousands of pounds. If you have deep pockets and a big budget that is fine. If you are on a tighter budget then the solution is to obtain the parts second-hand. You can do this by hunting out each part as and when you need it, buying the bits from a scrapyard or by spending a lot of time on eBay. The problem with any of these routes is that you could end up using a hundred and one different bits of different cars and, unless you're scrupulously organised, by the time you get to the end you won't have a clue where half of it came from and how much it all cost.

The best option is to try to source a complete car that you can use the major components from, but there will always be parts you may want to change or replace with new (for example brake discs), or you may want to throw away the instrument panel and replace it with a smart digital version.

Components required for the job should ideally be sourced from one vehicle. However, this may compromise the design or performance of your car in certain areas. For instance, you may end up using a steering rack that doesn't provide perfect geometry or a heater that's a bit more bulky than you'd ideally choose. However, if your intention is to produce more than just a one-off, then the selection of components becomes quite crucial.

Kit cars tend to use one single vehicle to obtain the majority of parts from. However, specialist suppliers can provide you with a full set of new components and, as long as they are sourced at original equipment manufacturer's (OEM) prices, this is not necessarily a cost prohibitive way to proceed. In kit car circles, these cars are referred to as donor cars. However, in this age of growing environmental conscientiousness and in an effort to win some sympathy for at least one set of petrolheads, I prefer to bring them into a more fashionable green era by calling them 'recyclacars'. We are, after all, giving a cast-off car a new lease of life.

■ *A donor car will supply many of your mechanical components – although perhaps the phrase 'recyclacar' is more trendy these days.*

■ *You may opt to buy an accident-damaged donor. If you take this route, a modern salvage yard offers good choice.*

If you decide to source a complete car (and I will go into more detail into how you choose the most appropriate car later) you can go to a salvage yard or purchase a car privately. Salvage yards are an education in themselves. You should investigate locations and types of yard in your area. The image some of us have of a salvage yard being a dirty, muddy, greasy, oily place, complete with Rottweilers is still not totally misplaced. However, almost all of these places will be overseen by a salt-of-the-earth bloke who has an inbuilt computer in his head telling him where every car and every part left on it is located, even though it appears to us to look like a chaotic mess. You will not be without the benefit of help and advice in most cases.

Generally, the best place to buy a complete recyclacar in terms of choice, service and cost are the large modern chains of salvage yards who you will find are generally well organised, well laid out with very helpful staff. Searching on the internet will provide you with a good assortment of suitable candidates for your recyclacar. Serious cosmetic damage on the lowest mileage car you can afford is the best recipe. The more cosmetic damage the better, as a car like this will become less attractive to a trader who would be looking to buy

one with the intention of rebuilding it.

You can search by category and price, and view photographs of the cars on offer prior to making a visit. Quite often it is possible to make an offer below the list price, particularly for cars which have been in their yard for some time. Usually they will be able to arrange delivery for you. You will, without a doubt, reap rewards from spending some time at the scrapyard, inspecting potential cars carefully and, if necessary, having a list of your requirements with you so you don't forget any important factors in the decision of which car to go for.

It is quite easy when you get there to get over-excited and make an impulse purchase and then realise you forgot to check the criteria list and something important is missing. As an example, if you remove the wiring harness and ECU from a Ford Focus ST170, it's easy to forget the fuel control module which is hidden under the passenger seat.

Due to health and safety requirements, scrapyards are becoming few and far between and those that exist have become far more strictly controlled. It is generally safe to assume that an accident-damaged car was in full running order at the moment of impact. Accident damaged cars are classified into categories and, in order to make sure that you get a V5, it is important to make sure that if you

■ *Taking many components from one car will mean you can retain an age-related plate rather than a Q. This is more desirable.*

■ *Take measurements from the engine so you can ensure you design your chassis to accommodate your powerplant of choice.*

buy an accident damaged write-off that it is classed as either a Category C or a Category D. No V5 will mean that when you come to register your new car that it may be given a Q-plate. I'll cover all the categories and their implications later.

There is a good argument for avoiding breakers' yards altogether. A road legal car can often be driven and tested before purchase, and after purchase you can become familiar with anything which may need replacing or fixing before you use it for your creation. You will get a V5 registration certificate for the vehicle which is very important when you arrive at the stage of making your creation road legal if you want to avoid that Q-plate.

Aside from the major decision of choosing which engine you require, you will need to inspect potential recyclacars meticulously. For instance, you need to look at the engine mounts. This is very important as you will need to get exact measurements off the engine mounting points to locate the mounting brackets on your own chassis, which will then correspond with the mounting brackets on the engine. This may appear as though it is a relatively easy task. It is, but you must be careful, particularly with lower engine mountings, as to where they will sit on your chassis. You don't want to find out that the only place they will fit is hanging out underneath, so careful planning is needed here.

It's also preferable to source a car that has disc brakes all round, particularly if the design exposes the rear brakes. Drums could be considered unsightly. It is not uncommon for varying years of the same model to have a differing braking configuration.

Check the gear linkage. If your car is going to be mid-engined, a cable change gearbox makes it much easier to adapt the linkage when the engine has been moved to the back of the car. If your

engine will be at the front end, cable change is still preferable but not essential.

The question you need to ask yourself is how many of the following parts is it practical and possible to use from my proposed recyclacar. Let's look at those parts and explain why you may choose not to take any specific items from your recyclacar.

Engine: First of all, you will need to decide on the output required from the powerplant. It is important here to remember that the power to weight ratio will change significantly when you take the engine out of its original car and put it into a car that could weigh anything from around 300kg to 800kg lighter.

This means that you don't need to look at an engine with massive amounts of power, nor do you necessarily need to find an engine that is turbocharged or supercharged. (As an aside, a turbocharger is a centrifugal force, powered by gases from the exhaust which pressurises the intake air and causes the power output to increase. A supercharger works in much the same way but it uses the engine to power a pulley belt which drives the fan to pressurise the intake air). The major difference between these two different methods is that there is no lull in the power increase with a supercharger.

A lot of people think that using a standard 1.6-litre engine out of say a Mazda MX-5 or a Ford Focus will result in an underpowered car. This is not the case. Put this engine into a 700kg car and it will be more than fast enough for road use. When you are discussing the car you have built with your friends and they don't believe it, just take the doubter for a ride in your car. I promise you they will be smiling when you come back and they won't believe you have an unmodified powerplant under there! I have done this many times, and not

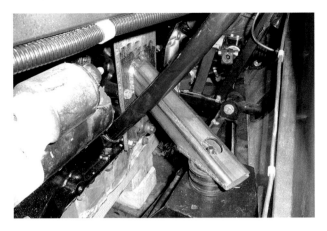

■ *Measure the position of the engine mounts to ensure you can replicate the pick-up points in your own chassis.*

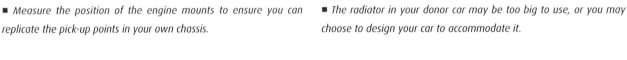

■ *The radiator in your donor car may be too big to use, or you may choose to design your car to accommodate it.*

revealed the engine size until after the drive out. My passengers are always shocked if I tell them this particular car is powered by a standard 1.6.

Next you must consider the physical dimensions of the engine. The best way to find this out is just to go to a scrapyard and measure some. You will need to avoid engines which are excessively tall and could make the design of your car difficult. It will, of course, depend to some extent on whether you decide on a mid-engined car or a front-engined car. If the engine is behind the cockpit you can get away with a slightly taller one, if it's in the front you will be much more restricted if you want the car to have any kind of sleek line at the front end.

The engine mountings are crucial and have to be considered seriously in terms of how they will relate to your chassis. You will need to have in mind your desired suspension layout, too, so that you can

ensure the transmission and suspension interact well dimensionally. You must also remember at all times that the you must incorporate into your design the ability to remove and re-install your engine once the car is built. Sometimes, this means the engine will only go in one way, for example with one end pointing down and sliding underneath a bracket welded onto the chassis to take an engine mount. Alternatively, engines can be lowered out from under the car for removal if the chassis is designed with this in mind. The measurements you take for the brackets which are going to be welded to your chassis to accommodate the engine mounts need to be very accurate.

Radiator: You will need to consider some of the same points here as you did for your engine criteria. The standard radiator from the car you are considering using may be totally unsuitable for your car because of its size. If you want to have a sleek front end you won't

■ *A mid-engined layout means you don't have to worry so much about the engine being tall.*

■ *Remember that the engine will need to be removable after assembly. This will have a bearing on the design of the mounts.*

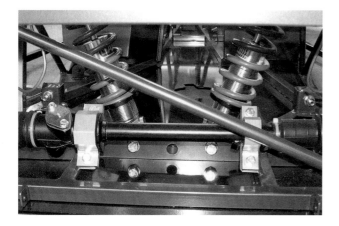

■ *The steering rack from your recyclacar may not be suitable if it has PAS. You may look elsewhere – a Ford Escort Mk2 rack is popular.*

■ *When choosing a steering column, it's preferable to source one that is the correct length without the need for alteration.*

achieve it with a wide and/or tall radiator. This is not a problem as there are plenty of aftermarket radiators available and you will find something that will fit into your design. However, at this stage you must also consider where the radiator pipes connect, which way the bends go on the pipes, where the brackets are on any radiator you are considering as, again, you will need to make brackets for the chassis to accommodate the radiator. The volume of water in any replacement radiator should match that of the one it replaces.

Steering rack: Whether or not you use the steering rack from your recyclacar will depend again on the model. Reasons you may look elsewhere include PAS (which may not work safely or efficiently without hydraulic assistance), meaning it may be better to source a manual rack from elsewhere. This may affect your steering geometry. When turning a corner, it is important to ensure that the wheel on the

inside of the corner is turning in a tighter radius than the outside wheel.

If you draw an imaginary line between the centres of the front ball joints, and the steering rack is positioned in front of this line then the track rod end centres need to be on the outside of the line to ensure the car corners correctly. If the steering rack is behind your imaginary line, the track rod ends would have to be inwards of the line. Arranging the steering in this manner enables you to achieve the principle known as Ackerman steering.

The steering rack should be parallel to the bottom wishbones when viewed from the front and above. At static ride height you will find tiny adjustments in the position of the rack make huge differences to the geometry, and if you get it wrong you could introduce bump steer.

Steering column: It is preferable, where possible, to utilise a

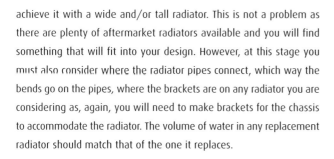

■ *IVA compliance is your main consideration when it comes to the steering wheel. Lots of aftermarket items comply.*

■ *If you're using a donor steering wheel, the airbag will need to be deactivated. This can be a risky thing to do, so it's best avoided.*

■ *Brakes can be retained from the recyclacar, but it's better to fit new parts in this safety critical area. Discs and pads can be upgraded.*

■ *It can be a challenge fitting a brake servo under a low-slung bonnet. On a lightweight car, you may not need servo assistance anyway.*

steering column that doesn't need alteration to the length. It is inadvisable to cut and weld a production item.

Steering wheel: The steering wheel is your choice. Your only considerations here are for the IVA test. If you're using an airbag equipped steering wheel, it will need to be disabled.

Seatbelts: You can keep the seatbelts from your recyclacar, or you may wish to have harnesses, in which case you will need to incorporate a harness bar into your chassis design. Either way, you will need to incorporate seatbelt mounting points and it is possible to put mounts in to accommodate either option.

Brake discs and pads: You may be able to use these from your recyclacar but you may wish to replace some items. Alternatively you

can purchase upgraded new discs and pads. This will depend to some extent on what you want to do with your car when you have finished it. Will it be just road, or road and track or race use?

Brake servo and calipers: You may be able to use the brake servo. It will depend on your recyclacar. You have obviously got to get it to fit somewhere and this can be a challenge when you are trying to get a nice low bonnet line, so here again you will need to do a lot of measuring to make sure you end up with an item which will fit into your design. Brake calipers from a recyclar may be used depending on their specification, but you may wish to consider purchasing new. Bearing in mind that your car is likely to be considerably lighter than your recyclacar, a servo may not be required.

Handbrake and cable: You will need to consider how and where

■ *Using an existing handbrake cable is unlikely to work, as it will probably be the wrong length for your new application.*

■ *Fuel tank can be retained from recyclacar, or you can have an aluminium one fabricated. It will depend largely on packaging.*

■ *Sometimes donor wheels look OK on a self-build, but most people will opt to change to aftermarket alloys.*

■ *If you're designing a mid-engined car, a cable gearchange is preferable as it's easier to make a mechanism that works well.*

you will mount your handbrake. This is not always as easy as you might imagine – if you're using an existing cable, it's likely to be the wrong length.

Fuel tank and fuel tank sender: If you are using the fuel tank from the recyclacar, this is fine. If you are having an aluminium tank made, it is useful to check the measurements of your recyclar sender and get the aluminium tank made to fit. This will be particularly useful if you intend to make more than one of these vehicles.

Wheels: Wheels from your recyclacar can sometimes be used, but it is very rare to see this. Everyone wants to upgrade their wheels. You will need to watch wheel and tyre sizes carefully. Offsets are important, too. The offset is the distance between the centre line of the wheel and its mounting face. High offsets may mean the tyres

rub on the bodywork or chassis especially at the front on full lock, and low offsets may make the wheels extend beyond the wheel arches. Don't forget you need to make sure whatever you choose will actually fit under your wing and wing stay design. Changing the offset will result in reduced or increased scrub radius and this will affect tyre wear, steering feedback and handling.

Gearbox and gearchange: If your engine is going in the rear end of the car, it is far easier to use a cable change gearbox. Some production models, the Ford Mondeo for example, used cable change from 1996 onwards. Prior to this they were rod change, and this is not an easy configuration when you are constructing a car.

Pedal assembly: It is sometimes possible to use the pedal assembly from the recyclacar. I did that with the MX-5 based MEV Exocet.

■ *Sometimes it's possible to retain a stock pedal assembly, but often a self-build design has a smaller footwell, making it impossible.*

■ *Retaining the engine wiring loom makes sense, even if you create a bespoke wiring harness for the rest of the car's systems.*

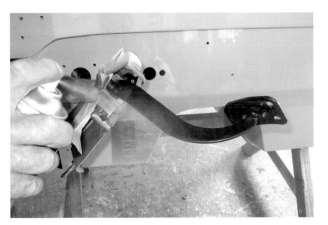

■ *Double wishbone suspension is the best option for a performance car. The Mazda MX-5 is thus equipped, making it a great donor.*

However, with our Focus based MEV Rocket, I found it was possible, if a little difficult, to use the Focus pedal assembly. This was because it was difficult to get the brake servo to fit, so we used an aftermarket Wilwood pedal assembly and master cylinders which worked very well and didn't add a great deal of cost to the overall budget.

■ *Aftermarket instrument options include digital dashboard and analogue dials. Your chosen style will depend on the type of car.*

Engine wiring loom: You will retain the engine loom from your recyclacar and in addition you will need to make up a wiring loom to cater for the peripherals such as lighting etc. We will look at this in more detail later.

ECU: It is often the case that an aftermarket ECU has to be purchased for a one-off special build and for quite a lot of the kit cars available today. This is costly, and can be anything in a range from £800 to

■ *Sometimes you can successfully integrate the recyclacar's instrument binnacle, which makes things more affordable.*

■ *If you buy a complete, working donor car you can test-drive it to ensure that everything works.*

■ *Even if your components all come from one donor with a V5 document, you need to use enough parts to gain an age-related plate.*

£2000. So the aim here is to try and build a car retaining the vehicle's original ECU. There can be issues with this and I will look at this in more detail later.

Instrument binnacle: Using the instrument binnacle of the original recyclacar can work very well. It provides you with a proper set of dials and is not too difficult to wire back in. You can also be adventurous with it and just use the contents and not the housing, leaving you to make your own GRP housing which you could incorporate to mould nicely into your dash. The alternative is to install a digital dash or aftermarket dials. Much of this choice will depend on the type of design you go for and the budget.

Suspension: With a few exceptions, you will not need the suspension from the recyclacar because they are often MacPherson struts. If you want to build a dynamically superior car, you will want to use double wishbones all-round so that you can adjust your suspension geometry to suit (this will be covered in more detail in Chapter 4). This does not apply to the Mazda MX-5, which has double wishbone suspension all-round. That is part of the reason it's fast becoming the donor car of choice.

If you decide to buy a recyclacar you must be aware that all write-offs in the scrapyard are listed in categories. Which category you buy will determine later on what type of registration mark you will be issued with for your own car. Prior to proceeding you must check that there have been no updated changes to the legislation:

Category A: Total write-off. No parts salvageable. One definitely to be avoided.

Category B: Write-off but parts salvageable. There may be a V5 available if your parts come from a car in this category but you will still be issued with a Q-plate when you register your car. This cannot be changed later to a personal or alternative plate.

Category C: Damaged repairable. This means that you can buy the complete car but you must get one with a V5 or you will need to repair the car and have a Vehicle Inspection Certificate (VIC) test in order to receive a V5 to use when registering your new car. A Q-plate will be issued to you if you do not have a V5 or if you do not use enough components from this single car (I'll cover this in more detail in the registration chapter). Avoiding a Q-plate gives you the option of later fitting a personal number plate, where as a Q-plate stays on the vehicle for good.

Category D: Damaged repairable. If you buy a Cat D with a V5, you will be able to register your car with an age-related plate. They take the year from the V5 and issue a different plate from the same year.

If you are buying an entire car, rather than just parts, the best option is a Cat D. You may be able to apply for a V5 if one is not present but you should check the status of the vehicle with DVLA before making a purchase. Ask if it has a VIC marker on it. This will mean it needs a VIC test.

For example, a Cat D 2001 MX-5 1.6 was purchased with a V5 for £550. It had very low mileage (30,000), and damage to the car limited to one side of the vehicle, which means there were quite a few parts undamaged not required for the construction of the new car, which were sold on as spares to recoup some of the original outlay.

One of the main considerations if you are building a sports car is the weight issue. Keep your car as light as you possibly can and you

■ *If you remove the engine from a heavy production car and fit it to a lightweight sports car, the power to weight ratio will increase significantly.*

■ *You can re-use an awful lot of parts from an MX-5! All of this goes into the making of a MEV Exocet.*

will see the benefits in the performance. A simple example shows the comparison:

100bhp in a one-tonne car = 100bhp per tonne

100bhp in a two-tonne car = 50bhp per tonne

100bhp in a half-tonne car = 200bhp per tonne

In order to calculate the approximate finished weight of your car you need to work out the weight of the components needed to construct it. I will go into more detail on the weight of the pieces you will design and make (or have made) yourself later but, for now, I will look at the pieces you will take from existing cars.

As an example, the Ford Focus 1.6 Sigma engine is, with the exception of the plastic timing belt covers and the inlet manifold, all aluminium and weighs in at a lightweight 80kg. The Focus has been

used as the recyclacar for several MEV models. The brake discs, instrument binnacle, steering wheel, radiator, handbrake and cable, brake servo, wheels, tyres, and ECU can all be used. The gearbox on later models is cable change which is perfect for a mid-engined layout and Fords make superb recycling vehicles. The Focus has been in production since 1998. Out of the seven years between 1999 and 2006, the Focus was the top selling vehicle in the UK for six years, so no shortage of supply for some time to come. You can transform this very reliable, very practical car into a high performance head-turner.

Another base used for several MEV models has been the Mazda MX-5. For building a traditional front engine rear-wheel drive sports car, it's a great choice, and available for low cost as they have been sold for over 20 years and are renowned for reliability. A typical decent example can be as low as £300, and this is going to provide you with almost every component you will need. Mazda made

■ *Dismantle your donor in a methodical manner and with an eye on safety at all times. Use axle stands, for instance – don't rely on a jack.*

■ *Once all the bits are off the car, label and store them carefully. It might all look obvious now, but you want re-assembly to be easy.*

almost half a million of these great little cars in the first nine years of production, so they are readily available.

When you begin stripping bits of your recyclacar, remember a few common-sense practicalities. The temptation that comes with the excitement of actually beginning this part of the project can lead to over-zealous car dismantling. It's great fun to dive in wielding an angle grinder and pretending you're Arnold Schwarzenegger in your own *Terminator* (the car destroyer) film but, I promise you, you will regret this approach later on.

The parts you need should be removed in a methodical manner. Exercise caution and think about safety as your primary priority. If you untighten that bolt, will anything fly off? Never rely on a jack to prop up your car, always use axle stands for additional supports. If you are removing pipework attached to the engine, get some luggage labels or masking tape and a permanent marker and identify the parts as you go along. The same goes for nuts, bolts and brackets, invest in some plastic storage boxes so that you can identify where they came from. You may have to drain fluids, although if you have purchased from a scrapyard they will have already done this.

Some cars do not have a fuel drain plug fitted on the fuel tank. If that is the case any fuel left in the vehicle will still be in there and it will have to be emptied when you remove the fuel tank from the vehicle. There are, of course, publications you can refer to which will assist you if you are struggling to figure out how to remove something. Take particular care on any vehicle fitted with airbags and always follow the manufacturer's instructions with regard to removal of, say, a steering wheel containing an airbag.

To be honest, sourcing components from scrapyards is my least favourite task, but not without interest. Having a walk around if it is not muddy is great... you can see all manner of interesting suspension/steering and engine layouts in a few minutes. Some will be upside down and others stacked up, so you need to have a good butcher's. You may well be inspired by one or the other but when you have decided what you need and from which vehicle, it would be great if you could use a single donor. That way you can get a car in

■ *It can be tempting to avoid messing about with a donor car and order all new parts – but it will end up costing more!*

your nice warm well lit garage and tinker away.

There may be compromise if this is your route though but, if you manage to source most of your bits and pieces from one car, then that is a good start. Of course if your pockets are deep enough it is much more fun to sit with a coffee and flick through endless catalogues choosing some nice shiny new parts that arrive on your door step the day after you click 'pay'. A much more pleasant experience than struggling with rusty bolts and craning your neck. You pay the price either way!

Chassis Design

FIRST THINGS FIRST. Is there a natural evolution of the car creation process? Three questions:

1 What comes first? The chicken or the egg?
2 Would a songwriter pen the music first or the lyrics?
3 Would a car designer decide on the body or the mechanicals first?

My approach has always been to let the form follow the function. Try it the other way around and you may well hit a stumbling block. Imagine trying to shoehorn an engine under a low lying bonnet that looks great but may be as much use as a chocolate fireguard. If you can't get your engine in, it's never going to be a vehicle. So to make life as easy as possible for ourselves, let's create the chassis first and then dress it to suit your taste.

Designing a chassis from scratch is not a job for the faint-hearted. I would encourage you to study this whole chapter before making a decision as to whether you feel up to the job or not. There are some rather complex procedures involved, but don't be tempted to pull the plug until you have fully absorbed the contents of this chapter. The chances are you will grasp it and get on with it.

Is a jig required? A jig is the frame in which all the chassis members are held during the fabrication stage. Making a one-off chassis will require extra consideration. If you have no intention of duplicating your work, there seems little point in productionising the methods. If you have a good, perfectly flat steel table that is large enough to accommodate the whole chassis design then great. If not, can the chassis be made in separate sub assembly sections to be mated together later?

Using square tube has got to make life easier. Clamping round tube down to a flat table is irritating unless you modify G-clamps to take a tube shape on one clamp face. At no time should you assume that placing components together and welding them is going to have a happy ending. Heat will distort your positioning if the items are not properly clamped. Weld a tube on one side in the middle and watch the ends curl up – not a good look.

■ *Large steel table is vital for constructing chassis. If you don't have enough space for the whole chassis, you can build sub-assemblies.*

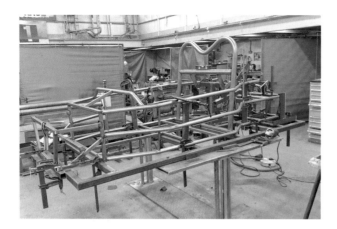

■ *Jigs can be complex bolt-together structures, using clamps to hold various parts together and various positioning 'stops' throughout.*

■ *If you are building a one-off and don't need to make copies of the chassis, you can get away with a more makeshift jig.*

Substantial jigs are generally manufactured for a production run. These can be complex, heavy-duty bolt together units. They will have clamps to hold parts and will have positioning stops at many various points to ensure accuracy and reduce the need for checking or measuring. Using a sheet of ply on a couple of Workmates is not

going to provide the same level of accuracy. A steel bed is what you should be using if at all possible. The heat is then partly transferred to the table and not your chassis.

However, a makeshift jig can be made on timber sheet. Take two 8 by 4 sheets of 18mm MDF and fully glue them together. Then use good screws to position stop ends and guide pieces. You can never take enough measurements; diagonal measurements to check 'squareness' are crucial. Once you have laid out and tacked together

■ *If you don't want to design your chassis, you can modify one from an existing manufacturer. This is a modified Sylva Riot.*

the base of your frame you can add supports for upper chassis rails and, once that section is assembled, you can add engine and suspension component supports to your jig to ensure accuracy. With the whole unit securely clamped you can proceed to fully welding as long as you are 100 per cent confident in the design. Remember, it is a real pain if you fully weld and then have to cut anything off. It is always easier to correct mistakes when joins are tacked together – that way, you can just whack it with a hammer and chisel.

Welding can be spread out to keep the heat build up down, seaming one part on one side only and then moving to another is the best approach. Forgetting to return and complete welds can result in a chassis going to the paint stage with missed welds though. It is amazing how easy it is to overlook your imperfections.

Production jigs will need very careful planning. I have been the culprit of struggling to remove a finished item from a poorly designed jig. Now that can be embarrassing if you specified the jig in the first place! A temporary jig made from junk or wood can take any form. If it is a one-hit wonder, and you won't need the jig to make more chassis, just rip it apart to remove your piece.

The development of your own chassis is not necessarily a stop or go situation. The half-way house approach may be for you to configure the basic chassis and then enlist the help of a suspension specialist to help with the geometry. However, it should not be too difficult for you to understand the basic principles of this so-called black art, and then you can experiment with either online suspension geometry calculators (pop that in your favourite search engine), or even use a set of Meccano and make a mock up to experiment with. This black art will then become crystal clear.

Should you wish to take the easy route and avoid this chapter altogether, it may be that one of the existing specialist vehicle companies would be more than happy to sell you one of their chassis, which we will assume will be well made and may fit the bill. But this is a car design book, so let's get designing.

Another way of reducing the input required from others is to create the basic form of a chassis as a drawing that can be presented to a structural engineer for comments on how best to triangulate the structure. I have seen these types of drawings posted on car forums and it's surprising how many people have an opinion as to how it should be done. In reality, there are more ways than one to solve most engineering problems, and it is best to listen to everyone before making your own informed decision. If, for instance, you make a spaceframe and add diagonal braces at every possible opportunity, you finish up with something that resembles a bird cage, or an accident in an exhaust pipe factory! The result may be a strong frame, but if two people cannot pick it up then you may have gone OTT.

■ *An alternative to a spaceframe is a monocoque, but it's a more unusual route for a self-build car to take. This one is made in GRP.*

We must not discount the option of not having a separate chassis but instead creating a monocoque. Virtually all modern production cars are this type of construction, and are the reason why there is a lack of cars available today with suitable chassis for use by the specialist car brigade. Mass production monocoques are made from pressed steel panels welded together, or from aluminium extrusions which are bonded or welded together, as is the case with Lotus and Aston Martin. Monocoques have been made in the past from sheet aluminium that has been cut and folded to form a structure. I have seen failures in this field where sheet aluminium is folded and riveted together in an effort to replicate the strength of an aluminium extrusion. I would not recommend you adopt this format as you may well have great difficulty convincing the IVA inspector that it is not going to fall apart through fatigue after it has travelled a few miles vibrating and twisting away.

A fibreglass monocoque is another option, but, for us low volume boys, this could be considered going around the houses with a hole in your pocket. The reason is obvious really. To make a fibreglass monocoque you will need to create a pattern and a mould, and more often than not this will be in addition to the bodywork, resulting in the two halves being bonded together. Highly stressed areas, such as suspension and engine mounts, will need careful consideration with either a heavy build up of matt or steel plates bonding in.

In all honesty, I would suggest you concentrate your efforts in the steel fabrication department. Aluminium is again an option, but it is generally avoided due to its brittle nature when compared to stainless steel, and stainless steel is generally considered to be inferior to mild steel which is more forgiving when you consider the possibility of long-term joint fatigue. So let us concentrate on the mild steel fabrication route, and first of all consider the following options:

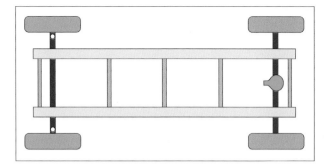

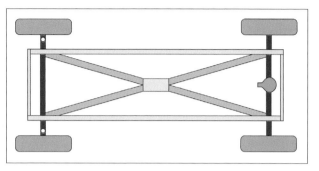

■ *Ladderframe chassis are ideal for heavy vehicles or those designed to carry a lot of weight thanks to high beam strength.*

■ *Cruciform chassis addresses ladderframe's deficiency of torsional rigidity with added diagonal cross members.*

Ladderframe chassis: A ladderframe is a very basic structure, and as the name would suggest, actually resembles a ladder in that we would expect to see two parallel rails bridging the two axles. These are connected together with cross members in a similar fashion to ladder rungs. The limiting factor of this type of chassis would be its lack of resistance to twisting (torsional rigidity).

This type of chassis is often used on pick up trucks and 4x4 type vehicles, due to its potential for high beam strength (bridging between the axles).

Cruciform chassis: This is very similar to the ladderframe, but an effort to stiffen it has been made by introducing diagonal cross members, these form a cross in the centre of the chassis, the cross effect being mounted on each corner of the perimeter frame. The limiting factor here is that your options for routing driveshafts is somewhat limited and the seats may well need to sit on top of,

rather than in, the chassis, which may not be acceptable to you.

Backbone chassis: In plan view it can be said that the backbone chassis is also a cross, splaying out at one end to house the engine and front suspension and splaying out at the rear to mount the rear suspension. The centre sections either side can provide adequate space for the driver and passengers. There is an option here to fabricate the backbone from folded sheet steel, which actually forms a centre tunnel as in the case of the Lotus Elan. Although another example of a well designed backbone chassis can be found underneath a TVR which can be best described as a multi-tube backbone structure.

Superleggera: This is an Italian term meaning superlight. It is a three dimensional frame that consists of a cage of narrow tubes to support the body which is often made from aluminium. The cage is usually mounted on a main chassis frame.

Spaceframe chassis: Also known as a skeletal frame or, in the case of cars such as the MEV Rocket and Exocet where the chassis remains exposed, an exoskeletal chassis. The fabrication of this type of chassis

■ *A backbone chassis can be found under the likes of the original Lotus Elan and late TVR models. This one is from a Gardner Douglas GD427.*

■ *A spaceframe is the most common structure for a self-built car. This exoskeletal MEV Rocket keeps its round-tube spaceframe on show.*

generally involves the use of multiple tubes (round or square), the advantage being that a carefully planned layout can result in the tube wall thickness being reduced so as to create a lightweight but strong structure. There are two key elements to a successfully designed spaceframe. They are the use of diagonal bracing (triangulation) and stress plates (diaphragms) used to stiffen what could otherwise be a fairly flimsy structure.

Three-wheelers: Are four wheels better than three? I have often posed that question to myself.

The answer is probably 'yes' in most cases, but we should not throw the trike option out too hastily without due consideration. Trikes can be great fun and can also cost less to design and build. Logically thinking they are devoid of 25 per cent of the major components. Take away a wheel, brake, wishbones, one corner of the chassis and a quarter of the suspension and the need for a differential and suddenly your creation becomes much lighter. The power to weight ratio increases and smaller powerplants may be selected, which can often be lightweight unit construction (gearbox is part of main block) bike engines. Now we are tempted perhaps. Bodywork is probably going to be smaller and easier to manage and regulations are much easier to comply with. Trikes are tested under the Motorcycle Single

Vehicle Approval (MSVA) scheme which is a much simpler inspection than car IVA tests and also costs considerably less.

Still not interested? Well how about considering performance stats of 400kg with a 150bhp bike engine pushing you along. Yikes, that is going to be scary and not at all sensible but my goodness talk about fun! This book is about cars though but never the less we should look at trike options too.

A reverse trike is a layout with two front wheels and one rear where as a delta trike has one at the front and two at the rear. The latter lends itself perfectly for aerodynamic bodywork but will be inherently less stable than its reversed stable mate. I have a Bond Bug in my garage and I love it but am not often tempted to take her on the motorway. I did overtake a lorry at 70mph once and just as the nose edged in front of a lorry, the side wind nearly toppled me!

So I have since always favoured the reverse trike option. Imagine the forces we are subjecting our vehicles to in a turn. If you get it wrong and turn in whilst your still trying to push the middle pedal through the floor, the front wheel on the outside of the turn is well placed to assist.

The position of the centre of gravity (CoG) or centre of mass becomes

■ *A reverse trike (two wheels at the front) combats the stability problems faced by a delta trike, which only has one wheel at the front.*

■ *If you're building a fast road or track day car, the important considerations are occupant safety and torsional stiffness.*

■ *Doing away with doors means you can have waist-high chassis member to help with strength. Just make sure you can still step in!*

of paramount importance with trike design unless you are happy with an economical slow speed cruiser. A rule of thumb is to imagine a triangle with a wheel in each corner and then try to design the CoG to be as close to the middle and as low as is possible. However, one very successful trike throws this theory straight out of the window, namely the Morgan with its front engine and rear-wheel drive.

One way to improve on this design would be to drive the front wheels. This would provide greater grip driving two instead of one wheel, but would necessitate the installation of a differential. That would add weight but an advantage is offered... Imagine throwing your trike into a corner and then being impolitely informed by the forces acting up on you that you have over cooked it and ran out of talent. The wheel on the inside of the turn lifts and spins up on the diff, it then bleeds off the speed and drops itself back down. Built-in safety – unless you have passed the point of no return.

A chain drive to the rear wheel from a rear mounted bike engine is how I configured the MEV tR1ke. The 'R1' is in caps as the engine is was from a Yamaha R1. This trike has proven to be capable of high *g* forces in turns despite appearing, on face value, to be carrying excessive tail weight. An optical illusion is apparent as, with two average weight people on board, there is a 50:50 weight distribution. The only drawback is that when you drive alone then cornering to the left it is slightly less stable than turning right.

So let's not throw trikes into the bin full of 'no way' possibilities. They can offer a very viable alternative.

WHICH KIND OF STRUCTURE DO YOU CHOOSE?

So first of all, let us consider the basic structure and what it is required to do. If you are building a race inspired machine, your concerns will be (a) safety of the occupants and (b) resistance to twisting to ensure

that the suspension geometry does its job accurately. If, on the other hand, your vehicle is likely to carry heavy loads then the beam strength that we mentioned earlier with regards to the ladderframe type would be the area you need to concentrate on.

We will deal with this first as it is the simplest. You can buy off-the-shelf 100mm by 150mm box section tube with a 3mm wall thickness, and with a little bit of cutting and shutting you will be able to create a shape that accommodates the front and rear axles without having a massively high floor level. When mounting the suspension on your substantial ladderframe, it may be sensible to introduce cross-members or bracing as these are the main load points. Somewhere in between a ladderframe and a fully-fledged spaceframe will be a road car with doors. The obvious problem here is if your car does not have a roof and you do not have a waist height chassis rail, then we need to concentrate on the floor section to give us a suitable level of stiffness. One option is to design a chassis with parallel tubes each side that would create a fairly deep sill but that would not necessarily cause ingress and egress issues.

What you are effectively doing is halving the door so that the top half will save you lifting your leg too high but the bottom half may well save your leg. Looking at this option in plan view and assuming your body style allows it, you could consider introducing parallel tubes either side. In the case of the Sonic7 this works very well as the bodywork side panels are relatively wide and this enabled me to run diagonal members from the top of the front suspension which carry the loads through to the top of the rear suspension, which is also the point where the engine and gearbox mass is loaded into the structure.

STRENGTH AND WEIGHT

An important factor to consider when producing a performance car is the power to weight ratio. Having said that, safety and structural integrity become more important the faster one travels. With this in mind, if your objective is to produce a strong lightweight car, we must consider that a spaceframe type chassis may only represent 20 per cent of the all-up weight of the finished vehicle. So if for instance, the wall thickness of the chassis tubes were to be reduced from 3mm to 2mm, then the overall weight saving for the completed vehicle could be less than 7 per cent, whereas the tube strength has been reduced by 30 per cent. It may be possible, however, to introduce additional cross-bracing tubes or stress plates to compensate for the weaker tube and ensure maximum rigidity. In order to explain this, imagine a cube made from cardboard. Each of its six sides can be referred to as stress plates as the individual sides resist diagonal deflection on a single plane, as indeed would a diagonal brace from corner to corner.

A cardboard cube is a very rigid structure despite its very light weight, but if you were to take away one stress plate or diagonal you finish up with an 'open box', which is considerably weaker in twisting (torsional rigidity) than the cube. Cars without roofs are effectively open-top boxes, and have to be in order to accommodate the occupants, but considerable strength can be added back in by fitting a roll cage with diagonal cross members between the top of the A and B-pillars (or front and rear hoops).

In the engine bay area we have a similar open box where cross-

■ *A cardboard cube is very strong, but remove the top and it becomes weaker. It's the same principle with an open-top car.*

bracing can be introduced provided it can be unbolted to facilitate the removal of an engine. However, you can also opt for a rigidly mounted engine block (ie without rubber mounts) and then the block itself becomes what is known as a stressed member.

The points to remember are that a roof adds strength and so does a roll cage, but they both add weight. Opting for a thicker wall tube

■ *A rollcage can add a lot of torsional rigidity to an open-top car.*

also adds weight but would provide a significant improvement in protection from a side impact, and may add up to less weight increase than other options. The added weight of the roll cage can be reduced by using a roll bar instead.

In terms of safety in an impact, it may be worth considering opting for say 25mm by 25mm square tube with a wall thickness of 1.5mm to the front and rear sections. If these are unstressed areas and provide mountings for items such as radiator, exhaust and bodywork only, then these areas will not need to be triangulated or cross braced, they will therefore act as crumple zones.

A crumple zone will only act efficiently if the centre section is stronger in design, or made from thicker material or uses a larger section steel than the crumple zones.

Various CAD packages are available to test designs prior to fabrication, but they do require specialist knowledge. I would encourage designers to consult a structural engineer, as their expertise is invaluable and their input could save you more in fabrication time and costs than the engineer's fee. The use of modern computer based technology considerably reduces the engineer's time input and can therefore cost a lot less than you anticipated. The engineers will use programmes known as finite element analysis (FEA) software and a good engineer will use

FEA to apply simulated loads to a structure that he has drawn replicating your chassis. He will be able to experiment with adding or removing components and compare the effect, for instance, of using the floor panelling and bulkheads as stress plates. It is highly likely that he will come back to you with several recommendations. Firstly he will no doubt have found areas where the structure can be improved and secondly, he may well be able to advise on ways of making the structure lighter without sacrificing the structural integrity. It may well be the case that once you have made 20 or so chassis having introduced his recommendations that his fee will be absorbed by your production cost savings. You also get peace of mind and someone to blame if it goes horribly wrong. Torsional rigidity is measured in ft lb per degree.

To provide you with some kind of yardstick some examples are:

Jaguar quotes 4000ft lb per degree for the XJS
Lotus quotes 11,000ft lb per degree for the Elise
Aston Martin quotes 20,000ft lb per degree for the DB9
Lotus Seven is under 1000ft lb per degree

All figures quoted are taken from manufacturers' own websites

■ *Once you've designed your chassis, you'll be able to place an order for the steel. It's an exciting moment when it's delivered!*

Realistically, unless you are setting out to break speed records, if you can achieve over 1000ft lb per degree you will have a perfectly good

■ *Round tube chassis present a challenge as they require 'bird mouth' notches where one section meets another.*

■ *A square tube chassis is more conventional and doesn't require specialist machinery in its construction.*

chassis for your operating envelope. You do not need to go into overkill with your torsional rigidity targets.

BUILDING THE CHASSIS

Once the structural engineer has given your idea the green light, you can order the steel and aluminium sheets. Aluminium comes in 8ft by 4ft sheets and I would suggest you buy 1.5mm thickness to keep the weight down and for ease of cutting. Aluminium sheet is not cheap so try not to over order. You can choose your own size and type of tube. However, as a guide 50mm diameter round and 40mm by 40mm square down to 25mm by 25mm are common. Your engineer should be consulted in relation to the recommended chassis material. He will specify options including diameter and wall thickness and material strength. He will specify either electric resisted welding (ERW) with a noticeable seam, which is the cheapest, circular hollow section (CHS) which is a heavier option than ERW with thicker wall, or cold drawn seamless (CDS) which is a better quality material. More

expensive choices include titanium or chrome moly.

You will need to draw up a cutting list to work out how many lengths/sheets you will require and then practice your negotiating skills by shopping around your local steel stockholders for the best deal. The day your steel delivery arrives is exciting. You watch the pieces come off the lorry knowing you are going to turn these inanimate objects into a unique sports car!

Spaceframe chassis are very popular amongst kit car and specialist builders. The MEV Rocket chassis is fabricated from round mild steel tube. Although it can be more difficult to construct because, in areas where one tube meets another, the end of the tube meeting it has be notched (or 'bird mouthed') to neatly fit onto the other. You will also see that both the Rocket and Exocet main chassis rails are rolled to form the slow curves, whereas the chassis on the Atomic and Mevabusa have straight tubes with fixed radius bends to create the shape.

This may be considered a matter of personal preference, and if you or your fabricator haven't got the necessary tube bending equipment

■ *The MEV Exocet is made using main tubes with a slow curve along the entire side of the car. See how this compares to...*

■ *...the Mevabusa, which has straight tubes with fixed radius bends at each end. Different approaches to the exoskeletal theme.*

then there are a multitude of firms out there, known as tube bending manipulators, who provide services at surprisingly realistic costs.

For instance if you wanted to make curve rail tubes in your own workshop you would need to invest substantially in a ring roller machine, which is going to stand in the corner gathering dust once you have pushed a stack of tubes through it for stock. The same applies to rotary draw bending machinery which, even second-hand, can cost many thousands of pounds, and you may well find yourself only switching it on once a month, whereas the guy down the road may only charge a couple of quid per bend assuming he has the right formers to match your chosen tube size. If you are building a car for the first time however, I would recommend you use square tube as it is considerably easier to work with.

For construction of the chassis, it is necessary to ensure adequate width and length be provided for a driver and passenger of adequate proportions. With this in mind the most basic and foolproof way of doing it is to put two seats on the floor, sit two average sized people in them and making sure elbows and shoulders are not banging into each other, then asking the question "are you sitting comfortably? Then I'll begin." Now you can measure the required width of the middle section of your chassis, and get a measurement for the required legroom for both driver and passenger.

■ *Think long and hard before incorporating doors into your design. They're a huge engineering challenge and add a lot to the cost.*

Whilst it is a laugh to sit on seats in the garage playing motor cars like we used to as kids making vroom noises, the serious side of this is to demonstrate that it's alright producing pretty looking artwork, but you really must try these things out physically with real life size people to ensure that it will all work in reality and not just in the virtual world! CAD is the modern alternative and provided you have all the information to enter, you can then design using 'virtual' occupants.

I am aware of situations where the CAD operative has failed to scale the person to the vehicle design and the finished car will only work if the driver has extraordinarily long legs and abnormally short arms. If using CAD, make sure all measurements are double checked the same way you would with cutting pieces for the chassis. Remember when programming if you put garbage in you will get garbage out.

Some chassis, particularly those using round tube, do not necessarily need a body to cover much of them, as they are aesthetically very pleasing. This is the beauty of building your own car, these details are left entirely to your choices. 50mm or 30mm diameter round tubes can be used to make a great looking chassis, exposed if you like – your choice.

For construction of your own chassis, make sure you have a completely flat surface to work on. It is an important part of the measure twice, cut once school of thought, that you sit roughly where the driver will be, and mark out how much leg room you will need, and where the steering wheel and pedal assembly will go, how much

■ *If you are desiging a mid-engined car, ensure you leave enough space at the front for ancillaries like the radiator.*

■ *It's important to get the position of your wishbone mounts correct at the design stage.*

width you need to accommodate you and a passenger. Seatbelt anchorages, handbrake and gearlever positions all need consideration.

I would advise you to think long and hard before contemplating building a car with doors. There are many reasons for this including the high cost, the difficulty of build factor, and the way in which the addition of doors is going to considerably weaken your chassis structure. You therefore need to consider the height of the side of your car. You want to be able to comfortably step into it without causing yourself and your passenger an injury! Check the dimensions of your choice of engine, or place it in situ and mark out enough room for it. If you have four old wheels to work with, put them roughly in place and you can get a feel for the wheelbase of the car (approximate length, which is measured from the centre of the front wheel to the centre of the rear wheel on the same side).

If your car is going to have a mid-mounted engine, ensure you are leaving enough space at the front of the car to accommodate the radiator, remembering again that you will need to be able to access the radiator, brake servo and balance bar etc later.

When you get to the engine bay section (mid or front engine) carefully check the engine mount positions so you can either fabricate, or have fabricated for you, some engine mounts for your chassis, remembering as you go that you must still be able to get the engine in and out once the mountings are welded to the chassis, and also bearing in mind parts of the engine that must be routinely accessible. Unless you feel your welding is of a competent standard do not undertake the chassis welding job yourself, take it to a fabrication firm or cut the tubes and tack it all together and then get a professional to fully weld it.

Regardless of whether you have welded the chassis yourself, or had someone do it for you, once it is done, check every single

measurement on it, eye up the chassis from all angles and check with a tape measure and protractor. If there are any errors it is less difficult to overcome them at this stage than discover them when your car is built. Check all the welded joints to ensure nothing has been missed or is still only tacked together. Check every single weld all around to ensure there are no holes and no welds have been missed.

If you are creating a full-bodied car you will need to ensure that it does not part company with the chassis, especially when you are doing 80mph down the motorway (not that you would).

I usually include consideration to body support from the outset. Often extended chassis rails may just end up in the right area for a steel plate to be added. These plates will share the load of the body – just make sure you don't skimp here. Cracks or crazing can appear in the GRP if you get it wrong.

■ *Once your chassis is complete, double check every measurement and eye it from every angle to make sure it's square.*

■ *Consider fabricating your own upright rather than using a donor item.*

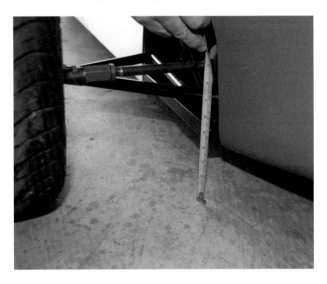

■ *Set the ride height correctly to allow full suspension travel.*
■ *Castor angle is vital to design in self-centring of the steering.*

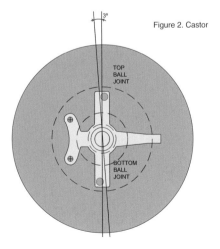

Figure 2. Castor

3°

TOP
BALL
JOINT

BOTTOM
BALL
JOINT

Suspension: Let's assume you are going to design a suspension system using double wishbones and coil-over dampers. You could consider using your own bespoke uprights (knuckles) rather than trying to find a suitable one from a production car. Many kit cars use Triumph or Ford front uprights, but you can consider fabricating your own or having them milled from a piece of billet aluminium. You must also consider the suspension mounts which will need to be welded onto your chassis.

Configuring the framework in this area is crucial so as to avoid deformation from heavy loads that may result in tearing mounting points off the chassis rails. To provide the best possible geometry settings for a race car or fast road car you should consider introducing unequal length independent adjustable wishbones at each corner with camber angle adjustment. You can fabricate these yourself just like most kit car manufacturers do.

It is very common to use an Austin Maxi ball joint for the bottom front pivot and a Ford Transit drag link for the adjustable top ball joint. The latter has a fine metric thread that can be screwed into a threaded hole in your top front wishbone.

There are lots of firms making poly bushes with stainless steel crush tubes or inserts, so the ends of your wishbones that pivot on the chassis could be made from tube of a suitable diameter to accept the bushes that are available.

It is fairly simple to make some 3mm thick brackets with a 12mm hole for the wishbones to pivot on, but the positioning of these suspension mounts and the steering rack are of critical importance. Unless you are familiar with the information contained in the following sub headings, I would strongly recommend that you study and fully familiarise yourself with all of the following sub headings instead of making an uninformed decision with regards to your suspension geometry. It would be a crying shame if you finished up with an excellent chassis that is let down by drastic dynamics which are a result of your failure to understand from the start the implications of the following...

Ride height: Your suspension should be able to travel up or down equal amounts to maintain tyre contact with the road whether bouncing over a bump or travelling over a pot hole. To set up the vehicle, you would need to remove the spring and measure the distance between full bump to droop travel. Assuming the springs have been correctly specified, when they are fitted the spring seat should be adjusted so that the shock absorber is 50 per cent retracted under normal load conditions.

If the static ride height was set too low, the bump stop may be reached too easily, and if set too high the hard ride may cause the car to bounce rather than compressing the springs to iron out the road surface.

Damping: The adjustment of your shock absorbers allows you to slow down or speed up the suspension travel. However, too high a setting actually assists the spring and can create the feel of a harder ride, although it is a personal choice as to whether you prefer higher spring rates with softer damping or vice versa. It is always better to start with minimal damping and let the springs do the work using the damper to restrict rebounds only.

Castor: The castor angle relates to the position of the top front ball joint in relation to the bottom front ball joint. If an imaginary line was drawn between the two it will lean towards the back of the car by about 6deg. This angle assists the self-centring but can make the steering heavy. If a car has only a couple of degrees of castor then the steering is unlikely to self-centre.

Camber: You should make sure that the camber on your vehicle can be adjusted on the front and rear by screwing the ball joints in or out. Excessive camber will cause the tyres to wear unevenly and possibly reduce the grip as you angle the tyre contact patch away from the road.

Sideways forces, however, result in the contact patch changing when cornering, and so negative camber (leaning in at the top) of around 1 to 2deg should be a good starting point. Bear in mind that camber loss occurs as the body rolls during cornering. This changes the position of the suspension pivot points in relation to the wheel.

If you draw an imaginary line between the top front ball joint and the bottom front ball joint, the angle between these two points when viewed from the front (as opposed to the side for castor angle) is known as the king pin inclination or steering axis inclination.

This angle (with the top ball joint positioned further in than the bottom ball joint when viewed from this position) is introduced to assist the caster angle with the self-centring effect on the steering, and also creates useful camber gain to the wheel on the outside of a turn. However, camber loss is introduced in most steering set ups to the wheel on the inside of a turn.

Camber gain: If a suspension spring were to be removed and the wheel were to be lifted by hand, it will be seen that the wheel will lean slightly in at the top. What actually happens in practice is that as the body rolls during cornering, this cancels out the camber gain achieved, thus aiming to keep the wheels perpendicular to the road.

Camber loss: In an ideal world the contact patch of the tyres would remain unchanged when cornering, thus maintaining the best possible traction. However, the high sideways loads imposed when cornering result in a tendency to induce body roll causing the wheels to attempt to lean (change camber).

Track width: The distance between the centres of the left and right wheels.

Tracking: Tracking refers to the alignment of all fours wheels in relation to each other and needs specialist equipment to set up with any degree of accuracy, although, initial set up can be carried out by bolting a three-metre length of steel bar to each of the front hubs with the wheels removed.

With 1.5 metres under the car and 1.5 metres to the front, you can measure between the two bars at either end. The ideal measurement should be around 2mm less at the front of the bars than the rear which produces slight toe in. Excessive toe in or toe out will cause tyre wear and also detrimentally affect traction.

■ *You can make scope for camber adjustment by using ball joints that screw in and out. 1 to 2deg of negative camber is a good starting point. This historic racer has excessive camber.*

■ *Accurate tracking set-up requires specialist equipment, but you can get a good starting point by using DIY methods.*

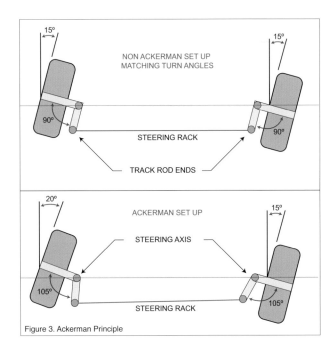

Figure 3. Ackerman Principle

■ *Ackerman steering ensures the inner front wheel travels a tighter radius than the outside wheel. Necessary as it's a shorter distance.*
■ *Oversteer is caused when the rear wheels lose grip in a corner.*

Wheelbase: The distance between the front and rear axle centres.

Ackerman steering: The effect of Ackerman steering is to ensure that when cornering, the inside wheel will turn in more than the outside wheel which of course it has to, as the two front wheels are actually travelling around differing radii.

This is created by the angle that the steering arms (to which the track ends are connected) are in relation to the wheels. If we draw an imaginary line running through the top and bottom ball joints, and then position the track rod end somewhere along this pivot line, then

roughly speaking there is no Ackerman type steering. If the steering arm is angled in, thus bringing the track rod end to the inside of the steering pivot line then it will have the effect of turning the inside wheel more than the outside wheel when cornering, but only if the steering rack is mounted behind the hub centres (axle line).

If the rack is mounted to the front of the hubs, the track rod ends would need to be outside of the steering pivot line. The effect created is needed to ensure that the inside wheel on corners turns on a tighter radius than the opposite wheel.

Bump steer: Bump steer occurs as the suspension travels up and down. The arc through which the track rod ends travel can differ from the arc through which the suspension ball joints travel, thus as the relationship between the track rod ends and the ball joints changes then so will the tracking. Excessive bump steer will be felt through the steering wheel, re-positioning of the steering rack to create an imaginary line that will run through the centre of the top suspension pivot through the steering arm pivot (steering centred) through to the bottom suspension pivot may well alleviate this problem.

Torque steer: This is the effect that the turning force of the engine has on the steering. Rotational forces applied to the front wheels during acceleration can cause the steering to pull to one side and also cause the steering to not have any effect at all if traction is lost through over-zealous use of the power available. Rubber bushes, often used to mount suspension units, flex during heavy braking or acceleration. This can affect the tracking and cause oversteer during braking and understeer during acceleration.

Torque steer is also induced as the twisting force applied to front wheels by the engine can cause the steering to pull to one side. If the torque applied exceeds the traction available on a front-wheel drive car then it will not steer at all as the wheels try to ignore the steered direction and just try to skid in a straight line.

Understeer: If a vehicle starts to lose traction of the front wheels during cornering then the steering input has less effect.

Oversteer: If a vehicle starts to lose traction of the rear wheels during cornering resulting in the back end stepping out, then the steering input would need to be decreased. Alternatively, opposite lock could be applied in extreme cases in an attempt to correct the oversteer.

Lift-off oversteer: As the phrase suggests, lifting off the throttle quickly whilst entering a corner can induce oversteer especially in rear engined vehicles.

Counter steer or opposite lock: Steering into the skid in order to counter act the loss of traction at the rear.

Moment of inertia: This is a term used to describe the resistance of a mass to change its rotation about an axis. A low polar moment of inertia is considered desirable in automotive terms to aid stability in cornering, braking and acceleration. If you imagine a dumb bell rotating around an axis perpendicular to its length, the moment of inertia would be much higher than if the axis were parallel to its length as the mass would be closer to that axis.

Centre of mass or gravity: This is the point at which all of the weight of the vehicle appears to be concentrated. If you were to balance your car on a point it would need to be directly below the centre of gravity. The centre of gravity should be as close to the roll axis as possible to aid stability.

Roll centre: The roll centre is an imaginary point about which the vehicle rotates. The front roll centre is generally lower than the rear, perhaps 40mm front, 80mm rear.

Roll axis: This is the longitudinal axis that passes through the front and rear roll centres.

SUSPENSION COMPARISONS

When comparing suspension types such as a Panhard rod connected to a heavy live axle, bulky MacPherson struts resulting in high KPI, trailing or radius arms which are unacceptable due to cornering camber angle changes, or De Dion tubes with limited independent rear suspension, it is clear that double wishbone suspension all round with camber adjustment is easily the best choice to make for a race or fast road car.

Trailing arm suspension: This system uses arms that generally run parallel to the side of the vehicle and are mounted to the chassis ahead of the wheels. Not considered acceptable as camber angle changes when cornering. Quite common on rear ends (also see VW Beetle front).

Radius arm suspension: As above but pivoting on chassis behind the wheels (see Range Rover).

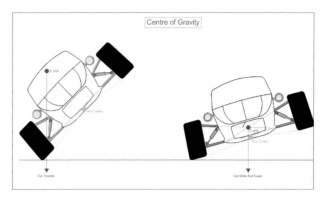

- *Centre of gravity is the point at which the car's mass is concentrated.*
- *Roll centre is the imaginary point about which the car rotates..*

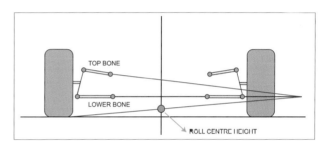

Live axle: A solid axle and differential unit with a hub at each end. Any bounce on one end inevitably affects the other. They are often mounted on leaf springs.

Panhard rod: A live axle would normally be mounted on two trailing arms. In order to stop the axle moving sideways on its rubber bushes, a panhard rod is introduced running parallel to the axle. It is attached to the axle at one end on one side of the vehicle, and attached to the chassis at the other end on the opposite side of the vehicle.

Watts linkage: This is basically a panhard rod that is cut into two pieces with a centre swivel. It is somewhat more complicated but does eliminate the slight sideways movement created by a panhard rod that moves in an arc.

De Dion: The differential is mounted to the chassis, and universal joints (UJs) are used on the driveshafts for each side . The suspension uprights (sometimes known as knuckles) are then tied to each other by the De Dion tube. This system does limit the independent rear suspension arrangement.

Anti-roll bar: This is a long spring steel shaft mounted parallel to the axles or driveshafts and is connected at one end to the left suspension arm, and at the other end, to the opposite arm. They limit

■ *Double wishbone design considered most desirable, with unequal length wishbones reducing camber loss when cornering.*

■ *A MacPherson strut can be found on many production cars. It's one to avoid on a low-slung sports cars as it's very tall.*

body roll, but are not always necessary depending on suspension geometry, shock absorber damping settings and spring loading rates.

Torsion bar: This is a type of suspension using a spring steel shaft that twists along its length, as opposed to a leaf spring that bends and a coil spring that compresses.

Double wishbones: Generally considered the best type of suspension for high performance cars, especially when used on all four corners. Provision can be made for camber and rear tracking adjustments.

Using shorter wishbones at the top than the bottom reduces camber loss when cornering – this occurs as the body rolls the and the suspension pivot points effectively change their position in relation to the wheel. This can be overcome be changing the geometry. Imagine the arc that the end of a short top wishbone would trace as it travels up and down compared to that of the longer lower arm that traces a larger arc. The end of the shorter wishbone actually moves in more as it travels up, thus giving us camber gain.

MacPherson strut: A long strut consisting of a shock absorber and coil spring connected to the front upright at the bottom and a body mount at the top.

Steering rack: Power steering is often not considered necessary if your car is under, say, 1000kg. If your engine choice has a power steering pump then you may need to remove it. However, that may result in re-routing the auxiliary drive belt. This occurred on the Zetec engines I used in the MEV Rocket but was fairly easily overcome with an extra idle wheel on a laser cut plate.

It is possible to use some power steering racks without power. On the Mevster we simply cut the feed and return pipes and join them with a rubber pipe. This leaves a small amount of fluid in the system to lubricate.

Alternatively, you may wish to buy an Escort manual steering rack. These are in common use for specialist car builders, quick ratio versions are available and the mounts are easy to fabricate.

I hope that by this stage you now feel confident in your ability to proceed to the chassis fabrication stage. Failing that, you should have gleaned enough information to give precise instructions to those people you will need to help you complete this essential stage of the project. By the time you have this wonderful frame before you, sitting on its wheels for you to bounce up and down on, there is only a matter of time before it's all covered in a unique body with your stamp on it.

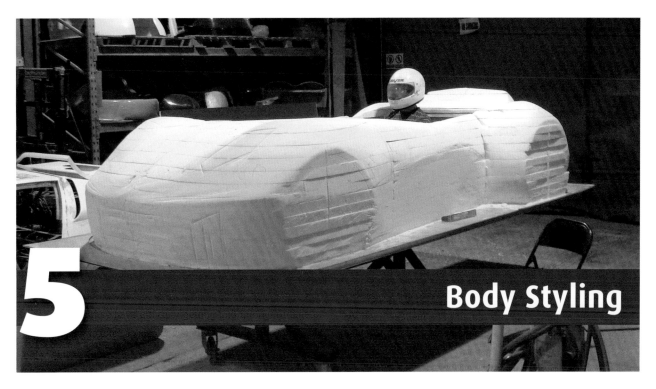

Body Styling

GETTING YOUR BRAIN into a creative gear may require a sequence of events to turn on the green light in your grey matter. You may feel you are not in control of the switch for that green light, and sometimes you may have difficulty getting into the right frame of mind. If you try to force an idea to manifest in your mind, it probably won't happen. But, if the timing and circumstances are right for you, you may surprise yourself and reveal design flair that was hidden in your sub-conscious. When I hit a wall, figuratively speaking, I try to leave the idea simmering in the background whilst I carry on with a more mundane task. Keeping the thought processing alive but not in the forefront of your imagination can often yield great benefits.

You may find yourself half asleep at night, quietly dozing away and suddenly, like a bolt out of the blue, that thought process starts to develop as if by itself. Failing that, try a hot bath. In fact a bath that is so hot it hurts when you immerse yourself, and after a while you start to feel light headed, you must carry on dreaming at this point and see if anything materialises. A doctor would advise you not to take a bath that's so hot that you go dizzy so please don't blame me if you have a seizure!

So there you have it. A little insight into what I sometimes do in order to get my brain cells active. Hopefully you do not need stimulating. If you do, I would not recommend a gallon of energy drinks or brain food is consumed prior to starting a task. Your GP would agree with me on that one for sure! Problem solving can be frustrating and the harder you try the more you may become frustrated and less likely to solve the problem, but if an idea comes to you jot it down, wherever you are.

I designed the basis of a car once while sitting on a beach having had too much rum and sun. I found myself in a very very relaxed mental state, and able to almost touch and feel the image of a car that was crystal clear in my mind. I would not for one minute go as far as to suggest the use of illicit substances to broaden your mind, but it is an interesting experiment to carry on doodling or dreaming even when the line you draw appears to have doubled or tripled due to excessive amounts of alcohol in your bloodstream. Once that idea has fully developed in your mind, or your doodling starts to mirror your thought process, then it is time to prove the design, but not until you are sober! This will largely entail making sure the body you've styled fits over the mechanical package you propose to use.

It is very easy to dream an image but when you attempt to transpose it into a scale drawing you realise that your mind may be playing tricks on you, and discover errors such as a lack of space for occupants or the drivetrain. Once proven, you will be delighted with your achievement and you may feel like giving yourself ten out of ten, but do remember the chances are that when it is presented to the public they can and often will be unkind, so don't even think for one minute that you can please all of the people all of the time. You may well be able to please some of the people some of the time though. When I hear adverse comments about my work, it tends to trigger my self-defence mechanism and you will find, like me, that

■ *You need to get yourself into a relaxed state of mind to get the creative juices flowing. A beach holiday is a good place to start!*

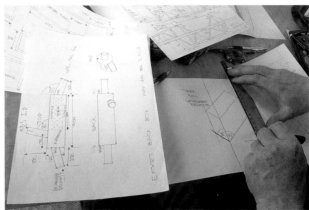

■ *An orthographic projection is a three-dimensional object drawn in two dimensions. It's one way to get your ideas down on paper.*

you can use what may be intended as an insult in a positive manner to keep you on your toes. Listen though, as you never know, a comment from someone whom you assume to be an imbecile hiding behind a keyboard may actually have a valid point whether you like it or not. Most of these comments would not be made if the option of using a PC and an alias were not available. Face to face they tend to be slightly less harsh – as they say "a smack in the mouth is often found to be offensive."

I can strongly advise that you don't take any comments too seriously as it is often the case that even if you presented the perfect product at the right price, the 'rude' critics will still not buy. If you offer a replica then the keyboard warriors may only be able to hone in on quality and accuracy, but if your car is of your own design it may well be pulled apart by those that are either jealous or do not appreciate your particular style. If the design you create does not attract any emotive comments, adverse or otherwise, then it may not be interesting enough. Feedback may help you to fine tune your design so take heed.

I am referred to on occasions as the 'mad professor'. To me, that

■ *You don't have to draw your design, but if you choose to some skills will be required. Shading and perspective are important.*

suggests I may be aiming in the right direction. I am not offended. I am not mad, but it may help if I were!

It was once said that the car I was driving only had one wheel nut – the driver! It's not too hard to see why. An eccentric driving a zany left-field motor, it's certainly difficult to argue that I am normal.

It can be said that if you produce a vehicle that is directly comparable to another then there is little point, as those looking for this particular style of vehicle are already catered for. To be successful as a designer, you may consider looking to cater for a niche market. However, finding the same is not exactly easy.

Daring to be different was a phrase I used at the start of the book. How brave are you? Moving the boundaries of car design takes more than a good shove but when you do create a work of art that is stylish, unique, cohesive, and well conceived it may well be seen as wrong.

One reason for this is that the car critics of the world do love to pigeon hole everything with wheels, "it looks like...", "it reminds me of..." etc. If your unique offering does not fall into one of these pigeon holes easily then the eyes may tell the mind that they are uncomfortable with the lack of familiarity but, as they say, beauty is in the eye of the beholder. For every person that finds your styling unacceptable there may well be another that gets it, and can't wait to ride in your off-the-wall creation.

The market will determine if you get it right. Lots have failed and very few can boast of a major success in the specialist car market. We often see firms come and go, designers dip their toes in the water and can spend many thousands developing their dream car only to find there is insufficient demand for it when they bring it to market.

My advice is to learn how to shed criticism like water off a duck's back. It may be the case that criticism, or constructive comments for that matter, levelled at you on internet forums could come from a ten

year old, a competitor or just Mr Angry who is taking a pot shot at you because you appear to be flying high. It may be that they too aspired to being a car designer but haven't got what it takes to bring their ideas to fruition, you have. To my mind that makes you the superior one here. You are the one who has or will put your money where your mouth is and got off your backside and actually produced something.

As I have said earlier in the book, my approach has always been to design something that I desire to have in my own personal garage and so, instead of trying to second guess what may or not be desirable to Joe Public, I work to ensure that I am satisfied. That way if Joe Public takes a dislike to it, who cares? As long as you get what you want. To be frank, I can't imagine the bank manager being overly sympathetic if you were to adopt my self-centred approach and fail.

So let's get down to the nitty-gritty and look at the ways of converting the image in your mind into a car on your drive. You should by this stage have formulated a car concept having studied Chapter 1 and have a platform lay out and a basic drawing with some rudimentary dimensions. Hopefully, you will also have a basic orthographic projection having used the one, two, or three-box approach. Orthographic projection is a term used for drawing a three dimensional object in two dimensions. Essentially, we are taking a vertical line down the middle of the page and showing an outline of

■ *Creating a CAD rendering is another way of creating your shape. Or you could just shape it physically.*

your vehicle, at 60deg to the left and 30deg to the right of that line.

Do not worry if you are not an artist and have difficulty creating even basic renderings. What you are trying to create here is not necessarily going to be of a standard that you would be proud to hang above your mantelpiece, it's about interpretation and scale and proportions. However, it may well help for you to hone your drawing skills prior to starting to work with materials in your workshop. When I mention interpretation, I mean that the drawing will serve as a reminder of your aim, and if others see something different from your drawing to your own eyes that is not necessarily a concern at this stage.

Improving your drawing skills may result in round wheels becoming oval from certain angles, and as you draw you will need to be able to shade in order to show how light may reflect off the panels, and how the vehicle will reduce towards the rear as it moves further away from the eye. The rear wheel will be smaller than the front assuming you are drawing a front three quarter view (ie one quarter front, one half side view 30/60deg perspective).

Experts in the drawing field will refer to a vanishing point and you must decide where that vanishing point is going to be. In other

■ *If you're building a replica, your styling is already done. You just need to translate it as accurately as possible!*

■ *Tracing a picture of a similar car to the one you're designing is a good way to get the basic proportions correct.*

words, if your car were 50 metres long, the wheel furthest away from you would probably be a dot. Whilst designing your body and trying to draw it at the same time, you may wish to enlist the services of an artist or someone au fait with software packages that can produce 3D renderings. Have you tried Google SketchUp? I have to say it's not for me, I find the process rather labour intensive and, as I don't enjoy the task, it is unlikely I am going to speed up and improve. I also find that whilst half your brain is concentrating on how to operate the system, then only half of it is left for you to design a car with. I would sooner get splinters and hit my knuckles with a hammer whilst creating a mock up than stare at a screen.

So if you are about to hit the panic button as you find this drawing malarkey daunting, I would encourage you to first of all read through to the end of this chapter and consider all the points raised, at which point you may wish to refer back to the last paragraph in Chapter 1 and continue to develop a mock-up to fine-tune your design.

Personally, I take more of an engineer's view and prefer to draw an orthographic projection based on drawings I have previously prepared showing top, side, front and back views.

If you are concerned at this point and are wondering how you are going to get over this stage, then I have a great tip for you. All you need is a half-decent photograph, taken from an angle that suits your purpose of a vehicle that is as close to the one in your mind as possible. Trace it.

This way you are guaranteed that your drawing is at least in proportion, enabling you to modify it to suit. I took this approach when I designed the Mevster, I went on holiday with a pack of A4 paper and a decent picture of the Exocet and an MX-5 and doodled away for hours, confident in the knowledge that the critical areas such as seats, wheels and engine position, were correct. I have to say though, that drawing the Mevster is easy because of its sharp contemporary lines compared to the curvaceous lines of the MEV Replicar.

I didn't attempt to draw that one! Not that there was any real point, because I was not designing it. Whilst we are on the subject, it is interesting to note that people looking at the Replicar say it is

■ *Look around for inspiration and you may see that a bus...*

■ *...shares its lights with a more exotic Pagani Zonda.*

■ *Aluminium is often used to create exterior panelling. This will limit your styling choices unless you're skilled with an English wheel.*

■ *Short front and rear overhangs can make sports car look purposeful. On an off-roader like this, it makes for steep approach angles.*

larger than they expected. I am continually pointing out that the track width and wheelbase is actually that of an MX-5. The Replicar, however, has very large front and rear overhangs, resulting in a fairly long bonnet and boot, but its total length is deceivingly just under four metres. An optical illusion perhaps.

INSPIRATION

My guess is that most of us have ideas in our heads that are generated sub-consciously having studied other designs. Your design may well be the culmination of many of the objects that have been seen as eye candy over the years. Not necessarily cars, but maybe you find the front corner of a Lamborghini or a side vent on a Range Rover has triggered your thought process. Maybe the silhouette of a stealth helicopter or the sight of James Bond flying through the air in a single seat boat has inspired you.

Working with a combination of various elements from a range of other products can be a way forward, but often the mixing of various styles or varying the design language may not have a happy ending. Taking architecture for an example, Georgian pillars on the entrance to a house with mock Tudor cladding and Victorian balustrading around the garden can be seen as an unpalatable mix.

Cars can be more forgiving though. The next time you see a bus flying past you on a motorway, have a look at the back lights. On some of them you will find the same unit that is used on the rather more glamorous rear end of a Pagani Zonda! So before we move on, why don't you formulate a list of your favourite cars, boats or aircraft and analyse them, until you discover exactly which individual items or areas please you? Then move perhaps to a sketch which could include elements from various vehicles combined into one.

There are a considerable number of individual areas to consider

before finalising your design. I will list the most important ones below and, where appropriate, use the terminology adopted by the vehicle design profession.

Choice of materials: Your choice of materials will input heavily on your design. Looking back at older kit cars and specials, you can see that aluminium sheet was in regular use to form body panels.

The use of sheet material of any type will severely hamper your styling options unless you are handy with an English Wheel (see 'Tools'). You may well be able to use rollers to form a sheet for the bonnet shape or roll the sides of the rear end, but any surface that is predominantly flat, or that only has a curve in one direction, could well reflect light badly on your gloss finished car. 'Flat' will also reveal even a minor distortion from where a rivet is attached or if a slight deviation in a swage line occurs.

Production car designers working with steel are extremely restricted as steel sheet can only be pressed to form shapes of a limited nature. When studying production cars, you will see shut lines that have become necessary in order to join panels that couldn't be pressed in one piece. There is often an attempt at hiding these joins around the edges of lights or the grille apertures, but the use of GRP enables you to create any shape you like in one, or as many pieces as you desire. Being too adventurous, however, can result in complex multi-part moulds, whereas a clever design would restrict the number of splits required in the mould in order to release your panels. Reducing splits will subsequently reduce finishing time and cost, and improve quality and repeatability.

Front and rear overhangs: A 'wheel in each corner' approach such as a go cart or F1 car would suggest to the eye that your vehicle is

- *The shape of your daylight opening (or side windows!) is important.*
- *A consideration with your pillars is to avoid blind spots.*

- *Surface language needs to be consistent. Mevster has sharp lines.*
- *A curved 'tumblehome' avoids a slab-sided appearance.*

very stable. Off-road type vehicles also tend to have very short front and rear overhangs to assist with ascent and descent angles. If the front of a front tyre were completely exposed with no bodywork overhanging at all then in theory, the vehicle could climb a vertical wall, but only if the rear overhang was reduced so as not to contact the ground. Obviously, this is taking it to the extreme, but as a 4x4 comes down a steep slope they can drag as they level off due to the rear overhang contacting the ground.

Daylight opening (DLO): This term is used by automotive stylists to describe the graphic shape of a car's side glass. Your chosen shape will have a major impact over your car's appearance, and whilst designing in this area you should have due regard to the visibility from the driver's perspective so as to reduce possible blind spots. This applies to the corner of the driver's eye blind spots and should also be considered in relation to the ease of reversing a vehicle.

Greenhouse: This is the section of your car that comprises the glazed part of your passenger compartment. You can imagine it including the roof and glazed areas down as far as the car's waistline. When you determine the size of your greenhouse you need to consider extreme options perhaps, such as a chopped roadster where customisers reduce the height of the pillars and create letter boxes for windows, whereas at the other end of the scale, you may remember the Popemobile with extended pillars and a tall greenhouse.

Pillars: Your car may have no pillars if it only has a flyscreen but, if it does have windscreen pillars these will be the A-pillars, followed by B-pillars forming the centre support of your roof and the C-pillars being the rear roof support elements. As previously mentioned, you should consider the effect of a pillar in the corner of the driver's eye and, therefore, the potential for creating blind spots.

Quarter panel: Often referred to as the rear quarter, starting at the rear edge of the rear door and ending at the rear bumper. What you are designing here is the rear wing and how it interacts with its surrounding panels and how, for example, the rear quarter may flow into the rear lights.

Surface language: The language is chosen by you and is best described in general terms with words such as geometric, sharp, soft, curvaceous, plain or busy. Your chosen language should be seen to flow through the whole of the design from one end to the other. Cohesion must be created to allow the style to connect areas such as the grilles and lights and wheel arches.

Swage lines: You may desire to run a feature line or character line through the length of the vehicle, perhaps starting at the corner of the front grille and ending in the corner of a rear light unit. You may ask this line to perhaps be seen as running up towards the back of the car, suggesting that it is travelling at speed when it is standing still. You may use these lines to draw the eye away from features such as door handles or side repeaters.

Axis to dash ratio: This is the area you need to consider in reference to the relationship between the front wheels and the windscreen. Whilst considering this point you may also wish to bear in mind the angle or rake of the windscreen. You can experiment for instance by looking at the side view and running the line of the A-pillar through to the front wheel, does that line sit on top of the front tyre as it

would in a cab forward design or does it intersect the centre of the wheel as it would perhaps in a sporty front engine roadster.

Tumblehome: This is actually a nautical term that refers to the narrowing upper part of a ship's hull, but is something you need to consider in automotive terms as the way the sides of a car round inwards towards the roof. If your car features a roof with relatively upright side glass, it could be that you are designing something without tumblehome, and if the sides of the vehicle below the waistline are relatively flat and straight this could be referred to as slab-sided.

The face: You will be giving the front of your car a facial expression; a grille being the mouth, the headlights being the eyes. Here you can introduce shapes that may create an aggressive face or perhaps one that is smiling. You can drive yourself insane trying to decide on a grille aperture, but it is without doubt an important area to concentrate on. An easy option would be a Jaguar type oval or a Mazda type smile, but try to avoid styles such as used by BMW, as it is very easy to get the proportions only slightly different with the result being what appears to be pig's nostrils. Avoid straight lines

- *Ford Focus ST's grille lends the car a stable stance.*
- *Mazda MX-5's 'face' has a smile thanks to its wide upturned grille.*

like the plague, as anything that appears to be straight on a car is invariably slightly curved.

Looking at the sides of the grille aperture, it may be worthwhile taking note of the angles introduced by manufacturers such as Ford with the Focus ST and Mitsubishi with the Evo X. The sides of the front grille on both of these cars splay outwards towards the ground almost leading the eye into believing that the vehicle has a wide stable stance. Some grille apertures are referred to as 'shark mouth' and it is interesting to look at the facial expressions of underwater predators to maybe give you inspiration.

The grille aperture has a function of course, and therefore I must advise you to measure the surface area of the grille of the car from which the radiator/engine was obtained to measure the airflow requirement which would have been calculated accurately by the manufacturer. You may be driving your car much harder than expected by the manufacturer who perhaps designed a cooling system for a motorway cruiser.

Whilst we are on the cooling subject let's consider the grille mesh. There are lots of options here too and again an area that can have an impact on your design. Take expanded metal and try a piece. Then try perforated alloy of various patterns. Bear in mind, though, that the open area of some mesh can be very low and so your cooling air flow may be restricted. You may wish to leave the radiator unprotected and leave it without mesh or you may consider a few round bars mounted vertically from the rear. Watch out, it may finish up looking like a set of teeth in that mouth, although if you are trying to create a cartoon character's face...

At IVA, if the inspector can touch the radiator with his 100mm diameter ball then it will fail. If your grille opening is only 200mm high you can introduce a 10mm bar horizontally across the middle to stop the ball having access to your nasty sharp radiator.

Light units: There are literally thousands of light units available at surprisingly realistic costs but, more surprising, is how their origins can be detected even when used in a completely foreign product.

I experimented some time ago with light units from a Ford Ka and, having constructed the basic form of a front wing to house the light unit, it became apparent that I was not going to be able to disguise the fact that the lights were from that well known small hatchback. I tried Peugeot 206 headlights as well, and finished putting those back in the box to get a refund for the same reason. There are bound to be lights available that 'fit' your purpose, but bear in mind that the curvature of the lens will dictate the style flow of the surrounding bodywork.

One option is to use conventional 7in lights mounted in a recess behind a vacuum formed clear plastic cover, as per the MEV Replicar. Using the same approach with two of the modern 90mm projector light units will give you the greatest flexibility. These can be positioned side by side, or above each other and possibly incorporate an indicator behind your Perspex lid. Turning to the rear lights, all sorts of manufacturer's light units can be used as an alternative to the universal units often seen on trailers, tractors and buses. If you look carefully at some of the offerings from smaller manufacturers such as the TVR with the Griffith, you may notice that the rear lights are actually from a Vauxhall Cavalier, but turned upside down.

There was also a Noble M12 and Caterham 21 with Ford Mondeo rear lights. In fact, many low volume car manufacturers opt for off the shelf lights from someone else's parts bins because of the substantial investment required to create E-marked light clusters. You may wish to consider the same approach by looking at everything and anything and possibly inverting them as an option.

The most important area to consider with lighting, having put the styling to one side for a moment, are the legal requirements, and you should familiarise yourself with the IVA manual before finalising

■ *Incorporating an existing headlight into a design is possible, but if it's distinctive it will be obvious where it originates from.*

■ *TVR disguised the Vauxhall Cavalier tail light units on the Griffith by turning them upside down.*

■ *Aside from aesthetic considerations, you must ensure that the lights meet the legal requirements of construction and use regulations.*

■ *Clockwise from top left: Noble M12 used Ford Mondeo saloon tail lights, while Peugeot 206 lights find their way onto the Veranti.*

any design. As a guide for instance, the bottom edge of the light emitting surface of the dipped beam headlamp has to be a minimum of 500mm from the ground, and the outside edge of that surface has to be a maximum of 400mm from the edge of the car. Interestingly, there is no positional requirement for the main beam headlights, and assuming they are separate from your dipped beam means you could mount up to four on your roof if you so desire. The Fiat Multipla has them located just below the windscreen.

The dipped beam headlight, however, can only be mounted up to 1500mm high. All other lights and reflectors with the exception of side repeaters, fog and reverse, must also be within 400mm of the edge of the car, but the minimum height for these is only 350mm. With regards to the fog and reverse units, they can be lowered to a minimum of 250mm with the fog positioned anywhere from the centre outwards on the offside rear. If you decide to fit the fog light near to the stop/tail light there is a requirement for a separation of 100mm. It must,

■ *Vacuum formed plastics are a good way to fair in headlights. This is the mould for lenses that will cover the lights on the MEV Replicar.*

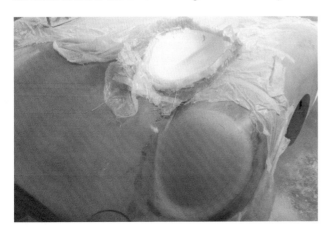

however, be on a vertical plane. To help balance the rhythm of the fenestration you may wish to consider placing the reverse light symmetrically with the fog light but on the nearside. Side repeaters do not seem to stand out like a sore thumb regardless of where you put them, but if you have an open wheel design at the rear of the vehicle or a rear wheel arch that stands well proud of the body side, you could run into difficulty in meeting the 5deg requirement for viewing the side repeater from the rear of the vehicle.

You must also ensure the side repeater is positioned within 2600mm of the front of the vehicle but, if it suits your purpose, it doesn't necessarily have to be just behind the front wheel as is the norm. If you are going to mould a mounting plinth into your bodywork for lights or create a relief shape for a specific light unit then you had better get it right from the start.

Pay attention to the IVA manual in terms of the sight lines of indicators and side lights. For example, a front offside indicator must have a clear sight line down to the nearside ground when viewed at a 45deg angle. This can be difficult to achieve but it is far more difficult to rectify if you don't get it right first time. Potentially you could be re-moulding and compensating a disgruntled customer. You would not be the first to do that either.

Vacuum formed plastics: This is a useful procedure for items such as light covers. In the case of the MEV Replicar's headlights, we first of all made the shape to house the headlights and then filled it in to form the shape of the plastic cover. Having achieved the correct shape we then took a cast off it in GRP. Then we took a cast of that to turn it back inside out to form left and right hand tools, and presented the pair of them to a firm with a vac form machine. They mounted the pair on a flat block and drilled small holes around what will be the edge of the finished piece. They heat the 1mm thick plastic and just

- You need to make space for a rear number plate for the IVA test.
- The R2 had a small frontal area to aid its aerodynamic efficency.

- Wind tunnels are expensive. You can apply theories without testing.
- This shows what happens to the air flow over a wing.

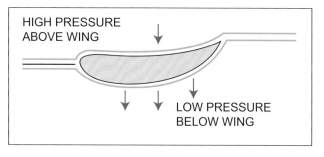

HIGH PRESSURE ABOVE WING

LOW PRESSURE BELOW WING

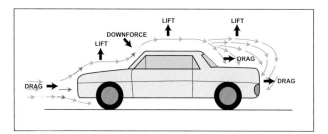

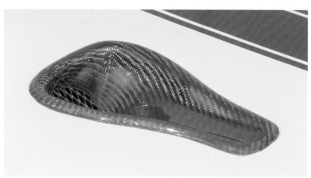

- This shows what's happening to the airflow when the car's in motion.
- If you opt to engineer doors, why not do something unconventional?

- When choosing an air scoop, think about where the air is being fed.
- Lots of seats available – style needs to be in keeping with vehicle.

at the critical moment they apply suction like you have never felt before, pulling the sheet down and into the shape of your tool. It's not expensive either. The tool is very low cost and the sheet that now resembles the curves of a lady lying down, may only cost £15 to £20. The two halves can be trimmed with a good pair of scissors.

Number plate provision: Provision needs to be made to house a rear number plate within your design. Some Cobras had to be modified to meet this requirement as there was only space for the rear number plate if a half circle was cut out of it to make way for the boot lock, and this was deemed unacceptable.

Naturally there is a requirement for illuminating the number plate adequately, and you may wish to incorporate a shelf above or below the number plate space in which to conceal flush fitting number plate lights, although this may not be necessary as there are now bolts available to mount the number plate that have LED lights built into them. There is no requirement for these to be E-marked.

Aerodynamics: Aerodynamics will play an important role in your vehicle's aesthetics, and as the term suggests the more aerodynamic your car becomes then the easier it will slip through the air. Consideration therefore must be given to three areas which are drag, down force and lift.

The illustration on the opposite page gives us an indication of what is happening as the vehicle is pushed through the air. Obviously downforce will give us more traction by effectively increasing the weight of the vehicle, lift being undesirable, and drag needing to be avoided at all times.

The effect of aerodynamic aids, such as a wing or spoiler can and do introduce downforce, but the cost has to be balanced against the induced drag. There are 'virtual' wind tunnel software packages available to help you with this very complex subject, but then you must consider that if reducing the co-efficient of drag (improving airflow) results in compromised aesthetics, you may consider the aerodynamic advantage as being a price that is too high to pay.

To make your car as aerodynamically efficient as possible you should bear in mind the following points:

1 Keep the front grille area small so as to minimise frontal pressure.
2 Keep the ground clearance low to minimise air flow under the car.
3 Rake the windscreen back as much as possible to reduce drag by improving air flow.
4 Car roofs with a fastback style rear window converging into the tail may reduce drag.

If your vehicle is to be shaped like an old Land Rover it may be as aerodynamic as a pack of bricks, but then that may be of no concern to you whatsoever if you intend to compete off-road. If your sporty type design is a screenless open wheel type (ie separate wings to the nose), then areas such as wishbones and roll bars and the driver's helmet will disturb the airflow which will necessitate increased power output to overcome the induced drag when compared to a 'slippy' car. Consider in-board shock absorbers, they will reduce drag (and reduce the unsprung weight).

Wind tunnel testing is very expensive, but I tested the R2 at MIRA's facility. The biggest improvement came from changing the 225-section tyres to 185-section. As an alternative to wind tunnel testing, there is virtual wind tunnel software, but that requires an accurate CAD model of the car.

Air scoops: You may wish to introduce an air duct or scoop to your engine bay, be it in the form of a bonnet bulge or side vents. These can be used effectively for cooling the engine bay, but a carefully positioned air intake filter may create slight benefits as you introduce the ram effect when air is pushed in at increasing speeds the faster the vehicle is moving. Do not allow the air to 'blow through' the filter as this can start a vortex and reduce air to your orifice.

Access: There are huge possibilities here and you may consider straying from the norm of a front hinged side opening door. Perhaps you would like to consider a gullwing, swanwing or suicide door, the latter referring to rear mounted hinges.

Perhaps it would be fun to have the whole greenhouse hinging like a Bond Bug or, for that matter, a front door as used by BMW with its Isetta bubble car. The options are endless, but you may wish to avoid convention.

Seats: There are various aftermarket seats available should you not warm to those from production cars. Style and purpose are our design considerations here. GRP bucket seats will not look appropriate in a '60s replica and low back race seats may not be complaint with IVA regulations. Consider the 'look' only and you may find a seat that is right in appearance but does not suit the intended use. A race seat needs to support the driver at the sides but a road seat needs to be comfortable on long journeys. Mostly a matter of personal taste but don't be tempted to go cheap here. I have seen plenty of sports cars with seats from a Cortina – and it's not a good look.

Instruments: Again a matter of personal taste, but we should consider the aesthetics from a design standpoint. A '60s replica would look bonkers with a digital dash and if you use the modern instrument cluster from the tin top donor it may be difficult to disguise. Dashboards of the '60s cars tended to be a flat wooden panel. Easy to replicate, drill holes in a piece of 12mm ply for a set of clocks and cover in leatherette or even the real thing.

Modern cars need cutting edge tech on show. That is not expensive to introduce now. Heads up displays will look space age but should you prefer the digital dash approach there are lots to choose from.

How about using your artistic licence and creating an ergonomic centre console? You can carry a theme through from the dash and house switches close to hand or even fashion a curved dash/console to give the driver that aircraft cockpit feel.

First things first. All you need is a pecking order list of required functions, speed being the only legal requirement, but how about oil temp, water temp, fuel level, revs, boost pressure, inclinometer, lap times, accelerometer, the list goes on and on.

Windscreens: The windscreen of a car is a very important style consideration due to its prominence. Thousands of windscreens are available from cars dating back many years.

Surprisingly, however, when you create your own style and pop

off to your local car supermarket with a tape measure (a) you might get evicted by the salesman and (b) you may find yourself disappointed with the measurements you take, as often you can find one the right width but then discover it is too tall or not curved enough for your requirement. Getting bespoke glass made is always an option, but it does tend to be a downer when a potential customer discovers that specialist glass is used which could result in replacement issues for him if your company goes to the wall – not to mention the cost implications.

Certainly, as a one-off it could be cost prohibitive to form a pattern and then to have a specialist firm make tooling to suit your exact requirements. Compromise is the key here, and it may well be a good idea to cut and paste or trace a screen from a mass produced car picture fairly early on in the drawing process.

Interior space: Your drawing will need to include accurately measured provision for the occupants, running gear, storage area and fuel tank. You will also need to consider at a fairly early stage where the exhaust will be routed and how it may impact on internal space. While you're at it, a car battery is a bulky item that will need accommodating. Check out the radiator dimensions too.

■ *Sometimes a donor instrument pod can be incorporated.*
■ *It's difficult to find an off-the-shelf windscreen that measures up.*

■ *If you're building a '60s style sports car, you'll need classic dials.*
■ *Sonic7 has a bespoke screen, but it's expensive to produce.*

Design And Build A Sports Car – Stuart Mills

Weather protection: Obviously you can overlook this area if your car is to have a full green house or, for that matter, is going to be an open top roadster with no consideration given to protection from the elements.

A halfway house may be the provision of a folding soft-top, a removable hard-top, stowable targa-top panels or just a tonneau cover to keep the weather off when parked and when driving alone with half of it open.

Exhausts: If you wish to extend your design flair to making a feature of the exhaust, there is no restriction. So if you wish to create a monster machine with vertical stainless steel silencers either side of your cockpit, you are permitted legally to burn anyone with them provided all contactable edges are radiused to a minimum 2.5mm.

From a user-friendly viewpoint it may be worth remembering that if you run a big hot can down the side of the car, it may well cause burns to the calfs of those climbing aboard even it has a heat shield. They will only do it once though!

Wheels and tyres: An important contribution to the overall feel of a car comes in the form of what it sits on, not just the feel of the road below but the attitude is often translated through the wheels.

When finalising your design, you could experiment with 20in alloys with 265-section low profile tyres compared with say a set of 14in alloys 185 tyres. The rubber band look on a 'Hot Wheels' type 4x4 is always a shocker but the choice is yours. Style, colour and size are all important points to consider. The application needs to work... low profile tyres on a 4x4 don't.

Colour: Now this may sound like an obvious point and one of personal taste, but I have often surprised myself by experimenting with colours. It's quite an expensive hobby, changing a car colour, and much easier to do if you have the joy of a CAD rendering to play with. Clicking a button makes it somewhat easier to transform a car compared to applying a gallon of paint. A colour change from, say, dark blue to dark green is just a cosmetic statement, whereas if you would like to emphasise points, or for that matter hide them, then the use of contrasting colours is often an important trick to play on the eye.

I always liked the look of the KTM X-Bow and loved the way the designers had 'lost' the body tub by colouring it black. However, I did see one of these cars with a white body tub and it completely changed the look and feel of those shapes. I made a similar mistake

■ Not all self-builds have weather gear, but it's good for practicality.

■ You can make an aesthetic feature of your exhaust.

■ A set of well chosen alloy wheels really lifts a car's appearance.

■ Or you can get away with using production car alloys.

with my initial Mevster. The thinking behind it was that white is the new silver, but quite honestly a pale colour does not show the interesting lines that I had worked on and did not do the car justice at all. More so, the contrast of black to white on my original car made matters even worse, and to compound these two mistakes I then went ahead and put a massive logo on the side. The interesting point was, when I decided to tone it down, I kept the roll bar black and

■ *Colour is something to consider as part of styling. Mevster looks a lot better in a darker hue than white. Note also how the black windscreen frame affects the overall look of the car for the better.*

then painted the screen frame black and with dark orange panels the car had really climbed a few rungs of the 'apparent value' ladder.

When considering colour it is worth looking at the greenhouse of a lot of modern cars, as quite often they use satin black in an attempt to lose the A, B and C pillars, blending them in to the flush fit glass. The colour of the wheels will also play an important part in the visual impact of your car, comparable to the windows in a house – see the change when those old sash windows are replaced by UPVC.

You may well be able to transform the 'old terraced house' look of your car by adding some bright shiny alloys or for that matter satin black, depending on where you want to go with this one. The biggest impact I have ever seen on a vehicle was on the MEV Replicar. We got the thing rolling on anything that was knocking around the workshop (just happened to be a set of tired MX-5 wheels) but then four minutes after the DHL lorry had departed, it was sitting on shiny chrome wire wheels, and that really did give it the wow factor. It's all about customisation. It's your car, it's your choice, all I am saying is that you should experiment.

Storage area: This is not a styling issue but one that must be considered at the styling stage if you are to provide space for a weekend's camping gear without having to ruin your streamlined dream.

CONCLUSION

I would hope that you now have something on paper or in your PC that can be shown in order to obtain some feedback from potential customers. You could consider airing your wares on car buff internet forums and ask for opinions. I have mentioned that you may not like what you hear, but then you can make the decision to ignore or listen, but do try and listen.

Take on board what is said, make a list and study each comment individually to see if there is any commonality worthy of causing a re-visit to any areas of your design. Generally you may find that these comments don't exactly boost your ego, but at this stage you can call it market research and possibly alter your product to suit that market. It's relatively inexpensive to use correction fluid on your drawing when compared to trying to correct the real thing.

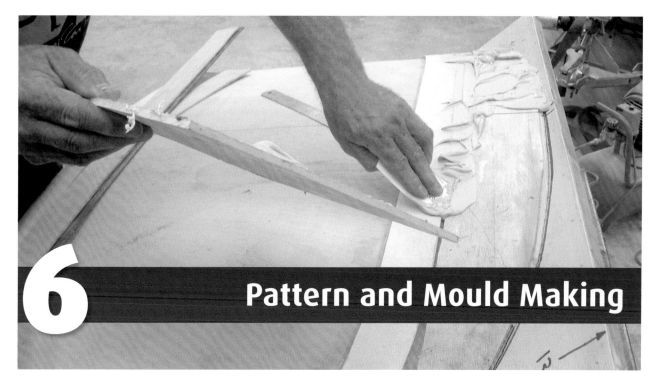

6 Pattern and Mould Making

CONGRATULATIONS! YOU'RE THROUGH to the next round. I would hope you are now armed with the penultimate design. Not quite the last one as it's inherently difficult to transpose all that is good from your drawing and re-create its full glory in real life. Sadly, there are bound to be areas where deviation will be required, perhaps wheel clearance around the arches will need modification or maybe you will discover the tyres contact the back of the headlights under a full lock condition, but do not worry, that is part of the development process. It will be a bitter pill to swallow if, at a late stage, you discover there is insufficient clearance for your throttle body or the

■ *A 5-axis milling machine is a very specialist machine and the most expensive – and most accurate – way of making a pattern.*

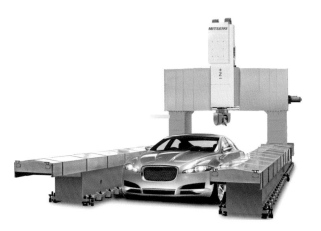

nose is too tight for your radiator. There are three ways to work towards getting it right the first time.

One way is to leave plenty of room around areas that you are uncertain about, but that may create unnecessary bulk. The second option is to ensure that you have CAD data for every single item that will be cloaked in the new body, so that a bang-on accurate shape will be created. The third option is to fabricate the chassis first, build it up to rolling stage with all the necessary components installed, and then build your body pattern on top of it. I should point out that a 'buck' or a 'plug' or a 'pattern' is the same thing. It is basically a full scale model for you to take a mould from.

There are five more options to consider when deciding how you will make your pattern and what you will make it from.

Option one assumes you go down the CAD route and have all the information available, or have carried out a 3D scan of your rolling chassis to enable the data to be used to control the cutting head of a 5-axis CNC milling machine.

This is a very specialist area and undoubtedly by far the most expensive way to go about this task. However, assuming the data is correctly programmed (garbage in will produce garbage out), you will be guaranteed a high quality 99.9 per cent symmetrical foam pattern. The polyurethane foam finish itself would then need considerable prep, with high build resins and primers to ensure that the completed item is stable and non-porous, prior to the waxing that is required to release the mould.

■ *You can use modelling clay to create a pattern. Beneath the shape there will be a wooden former onto which the shape is added.*

Most firms do not have the capacity to three-dimensionally cut a full-size car and, even if they did, removable panels such as doors, a bonnet and a boot lid would have to be made separately so that the openings and side edges have the required return flanges on them.

Option two is to form your pattern from modelling clay. There are various ways of going about this but the easiest process is to form a substantial wooden inner framework and dress it in chicken mesh or expanded metal. The advantage with clay is the ease with which it can be altered and, whilst you could very easily get through a ton of it, it is relatively inexpensive, a joy to work with and fairly stable once dry.

Taking a mould off it is a different matter as it would also need a serious build up of paint, and the difficulty being that if you try and move it to a spray booth it is likely to crack on the way, assuming you're strong enough to push it and the castors didn't fall off!

Option three is an interesting alternative which uses wooden templates that interlock to form a honeycomb structure. The holes can then be filled with expanding foam and then sanded down until the wood and formers are reached at all points. Scale models can

also be made in this way so that you can get an idea of the finished product without the finished price.

Option four is similar to option three but, instead of filling the wooden structure with expanding polystyrene foam, an aluminium skin is shaped to fit. It may well be that the wooden structure needs to be more substantial. This is known as a hammer form buck.

Forming a pattern from timber on top of the actual running gear is option five, and I certainly would recommend this approach be adopted for one-offs or proposed low volume production. The main reasons being that the cost can be relatively low, alterations relatively easy, the weight is far less than clay, and you will not drop yourself in it in terms of clearance issues. You will be able to keep the bodywork tight around the mechanical parts, but don't forget to allow for the fact the engine rocks on its rubber mounts.

It can make a huge difference to the aesthetics of a vehicle if you are able to reduce, say, the bonnet height, by as little as 10mm. If you hazard a guess whilst following the procedures in options one and two, the chances are you will be far more generous with clearance allowances. So let's concentrate further on option five.

In your workshop, your chassis will be sitting on its wheels with all the running gear mounted and ready for you to start creating your

■ *The buck from which a GRP mould is taken.*

■ *Maintaining symmetry is important at this stage.*

dream. Initially you will need to create a substantial wooden frame roughly mirroring the proposed finished article, but it needs to be solid. Bolting it to the chassis should mean that you will be able to move the whole thing into a paint shop or over to a fibreglass laminator at a later stage without it cracking or falling apart.

It is unlikely that you will be creating any genuine straight flat surfaces. Every inch of your panelling will need to reflect light across its surface, and introducing even the slightest curvature will ensure panel distortion is minimised. You may wish to obtain a couple of sheets of flex ply. You can buy this in 2440mm by 1220mm (8ft by 4ft) sheets, 3mm or 5mm thick and you will note that each of the three layers that are laminated together have the grain running in the same direction.

When dressing wooden formers with this ply, you will be able to force a curve in two directions although, depending on the direction of the grain, it will curve much more one way than the other. I always use an electric pin/staple gun and plenty of wood glue to bang these panels into place, and you will soon get an idea of how far it will go without putting up a fight. You could create a circle with this stuff as small as 3in in diameter, but with the grain going the other way you may be limited to a curve that rises say 50mm at the centre of a 1 metre long straight edge. The formers themselves are easy to make. Some 75mm by 50mm (3ft by 2ft) timbers, and a long blade in your jigsaw is all you need to introduce slow curves into the form. Remember to use larger section timbers for the corners so you will be able to sand them back to create a rad without it all dropping to bits.

You should consider symmetry right from the outset as, whilst the basic panelling we are creating with the flex ply may well be altered considerably, it is always a good idea to cut a former for the left and right simultaneously, then hold them together to ensure they match before fitting them to your framework. The same applies with the flex ply.

If you are cutting a tapering strip to form the top of a wheelarch for one side, flip it over and mark around it onto a spare piece in readiness for 'duplication' of the mirror image. Once the whole frame is clad, it's time to step back and check your proportions to make sure you are still comfortable. At this early stage, it's relatively easy to make substantial modifications if what you have before you has any unfortunate flaws.

A good tip for studying any inadequacies is to take your drawings and hang them at an appropriate distance in front of the car, so that when you stand back and look towards the car you should be able to match the size of the car to the drawing that is nearer to you. Maybe the real life object will appear to show weak areas of the design that you drew in the first place

The next stage is to get the detail right, but cutting out holes for the lights, door handles and windows is not a good idea, as all openings will need to be closed to take a mould from it. A windscreen frame mould, for instance, will effectively need a windscreen in it to keep the mould stiff and stable. So with the basic form in front of you, you will now need to invest heavily in a fair old quantity of Easy Sand body filler.

If I am working on a bonnet, for example, I will mix half of a large tin of filler, pile the whole lot on at one end, and then use a strip of stainless or aluminium, maybe up to a metre long, to spread the large dollop in one hit. If you try to cover large surfaces in a piece-meal fashion you will find yourself chasing your tail as you continually fill and sand to try and achieve that one swipe or drag standard.

Once you are happy that it is symmetrical and half right, you will need to hit it with a DA sander (dual action or random orbital). I use an electric one with 40-grit 6in pads. These will rip any excess filler off very quickly, so don't go mad or you will finish up having to put it all back on again. It should be starting to look quite reasonable

■ *It's best to design your body around the mechanical package to ensure it all fits. This avoids clashes and the risk of being over-cautious.*

now, but as you run your fingers across the surface you will be able to feel imperfections, and the way to address these is by hand, with 80-grit paper wrapped around a 12in block of timber. Block sanding in various directions will knock all the high spots off until the whole surface is even or, failing that, the block sanding process will reveal any low areas that need building up with filler.

Once you get the surface prepped up to a 120-grit standard, it's time to apply some high build primer. I use Reface which is a two-pack polyester paint that I apply with a 4in sheepskin paint roller. This is very rewarding because, when you have finished painting and it's still shining wet, your car will start to come to life as, for the first time, it will all be one colour. Previously you will have been staring for weeks on end at a body that resembles a patchwork quilt made of wood, filler and any other material you have introduced to help create the shape.

So coming back to that original shape, if it can't be made with flex ply you should look at every surface on every item around the home

■ *Flex ply can be used to create the basic shape, but almost anything is viable.*

or workshop and in the local DIY shops. It's quite possible that the bottom of a plastic dustbin or the corner of a plastic storage box or even half a saucepan, will give you the shape you are looking for. To be honest it'll start looking like a complete amateur bodge in the initial stages, but remember, it doesn't matter what it comprises under the skin.

Beauty is only skin deep, and underneath this particular skin you may well find some bits of old driftwood you found floating down the local canal! Joking apart, any wood that you introduce needs to be bone dry, we don't want it twisting, warping or cracking as it becomes acclimatised to your garage environment. In the event that you find yourself struggling to find a suitable shape, you may prefer to bond in a block of polyurethane foam and sand it to shape. Alternatively, you could use body filler to stick a block of polystyrene in and then trim it with a hot blade. For fine detail work, there is a specialist wood available which is similar to balsa called jelutong. It is classed as a hardwood due to its density but is very easy to carve and sand into shape. It's quite expensive though compared to the packaging that comes with, say, a new washing machine!

At the rear corner of the Mevster I picked up a pair of light units from a Smart Roadster, bonded them in vertically instead of horizontally and then fiddled about with some body filler until my heart was content. When you are satisfied 100 per cent with the appearance of your creation, it's quite possible that you will be able to see a glimmer of light at the end of the car design tunnel.

The next stage is to flat that Reface and correct any minor imperfections that have now jumped out at you. If you are prepared to carry the finishing work over to the mould and then over to your finished panels then the prep work on your pattern may well have just come to a resounding halt.

If your mould maker is going to use a PVA release agent then the finished internal surface will be matt and not perfectly smooth. In turn this will result in the panels being cast from it mirroring that same surface. Personally I much prefer to shell out a few extra quid in the initial stages and get a high gloss spray finish on the pattern. You could get a mate round with a small compressor and a gallon of synthetic lorry paint to achieve a fairly high standard at a relatively low cost. You will still need to flat it with wet and dry and polish it before you take the mould but, in doing so, the mould will be almost bang-on, resulting in the finishing required on your panels to be minimal.

MOULDING

The moulding process is something that I would not recommend you to try at home. It's not desperately skillful, but there are many pitfalls. If you make a mistake with the catalyst for instance, and add

■ *Sanding block used to fine-tune the shape of the filler.*

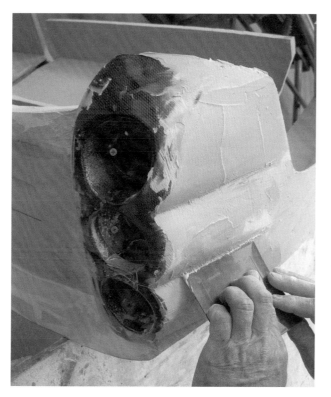

■ *Reface is used to finish the final shape.*

too much to the resin it may well create excessive heat during curing that could cause it to crack or craze and these lines, no matter how small, will be noticed on your finished panels. Another pitfall can be extremely painful – waxing. No, we're not talking about preparation for the beach!

If a small pocket of the pattern surface has an insufficient build up of wax, this may well cause you to have enormous trouble

■ *Tail light was taken from a Smart Roadster, turned on its end and used as a basis for the Mevster's rear light units.*

releasing the mould. I once made a new pattern for an aerodynamic rear cover on the MX150R (race Exocet). I was so delighted when I had completed it that I couldn't wait to take a mould so, having spent an hour or so frantically rubbing wax all over the place, I got stuck in with the GRP. 'Stuck in' is the operative phrase, as the following day I battled for hours trying to remove the pattern, and bashing away with hammers and chisels on the inside of your mould is never going to have a happy ending. I would suggest that unless you are pretty hot at this GRP laminating game, you enlist the help of a pro. They will be able to look at your shapely piece and decide where the moulds will need splitting in order to remove the panels.

Careful consideration will be given to ensure that none of the return edges are going to cause it to trap, and if they are not sure they will run a bead of plasticine around the corners before finalising the split line positions.

They will then throw a 2in flange up on the lines, possibly made from strips of 3mm ply trimmed to tightly fit the contours, and hold them at 90deg to your surfaces with temporary triangular blocks to the back side. Once the front of that section is laid up, the ply flange will be removed leaving half of your mould in situ ready for the next part of the mould to be cast, which will join on the split line. Wax will be applied to the up stand created by the flange so it will in fact split.

Once the whole mould is completed, it will then have three or four layers of resin-soaked chopped strand glass matt. In addition, it is often a good idea to add some stress members to stiffen the mould panels up. Maybe a 3in by 2in timber placed diagonally will be used and laminated into the structure. Bolt holes are then drilled through the split flanges. Next comes a very exciting, but actually quite daunting, moment. This is when plastic wedges are hammered into the split flanges in the hope that your newly formed mould will separate from your pattern. The result should be, all things being

- *This is the Mevster's bonnet mould taken from the buck.*
- *After all work, this buck was destroyed when making a mould.*

- *Here's a fibreglass panel being laid up.*
- *Don't forget to incorporate outriggers onto the chassis to fit body.*

equal, that you will be presented with a beautiful mould that resembles an inside out car.

There may be some damage incurred along the way to the corners of the mould, not to mention your wallet, but the saddest thing of all is when you see the pattern that you have spent many months working on destroyed. It has served its purpose but now it has become skip fodder. But let's concentrate on the mould, that is the important thing here.

If you spot any imperfections, now is the time to polish them out. If you are going for gloss, it will need some elbow grease, but it will be worth it. Get this right once by spending a few hours on it or somebody will need to spend a few hours every time you take a panel from it.

So we are now at the stage where we can lay-up the first body panels. The first one is always going to be the most difficult one to release, but you have proved it's possible by removing the pattern. The colour choice is endless and pigment of virtually any colour can be added to a clear gel, creating a paint-free car. Silver can be a nightmare and metallics should be avoided, so I would say if you are looking for a pearlescent finish on your car it's best to start off with a decent gelcoat and build your car to a driveable standard before giving it a final lick of paint.

You're far less likely to damage your pride and joy by dropping a spanner or slipping with a drill if you paint it last thing. The suspense will be almost unbearable and the excitement intense as you watch your laminator painstakingly lay-up that car of yours. They will spend a considerable amount of time with a roller applying resin to a couple of layers of 2oz matt. They will continue rolling to iron out all the air bubbles that may be present in an effort to ensure a pinhole-free gelcoat finish, that can be polished to perfection, assuming you still have some elbow grease left. When your car body finally pops out of its mould to greet you, the chances are that you will be so enthusiastic that you won't even notice that your elbow is aching as you polish away.

Now all you need to do is marry your GRP to your chassis. This is not easy unless you planned ahead. Outriggers are a common solution. These will span from the chassis out to your body at sill level for securing under each side with bolts or rivets. Support is vitally important – the last thing you want to spot whilst your polishing your beauty is cracks or crazing due to pin point loads from the mounting points. Far better to spread the load. Don't get complicated or replication may be an issue, but do give it support at the top, under the dash and around the rear bulkhead. Find places like behind the number plates to hide bolts too. Any opening panel will need adequate support too, door hinges are a black spot. Drivers tend to lean on doors when getting in. How dare they!

■ *This is the wooden pattern (buck) used to make the body mould for the MEV Replicar.*

You will have now reached that milestone and can stand back and admire your work. Try to be positive here, it really is too late to change it, but it's all about forward planning. I sincerely hope that at this stage you are nothing short of delighted with what is before you. All you have to do now is make it roll.

This book covers the elements of design in the car and not the building of the same. It is assumed that you are quite handy with the spanners and having designed a chassis and body around your chosen power plant, all you need to do is slot it together. That all is a big word isn't it? It could take anywhere between 100 and 500 hours to complete the task depending on the complexity of what you have before you and your ability. Don't let this sound daunting, I never really consider myself a car mechanic. I was self taught out of

necessity due to garage repair charges when I had my first car at the age of 17. The fact is that you don't need to diagnose and repair anything assuming it wasn't broken in the first place. Your task is merely, and I use that word lightly, one of transplanting components. The only problems you may come across could well have been created by yourself if bolts don't line up etc. The chances are that if you created the problem you are the only one who will be able to sort it out but, hopefully, the contents of this book will help to ensure that you don't encounter any major head-banging moments.

The building task itself could well be a long and winding road, so you must take each task as an individual item rather than trying to concern yourself with all the possible issues in one go. One thing is for sure: as that vehicle of yours starts to progress, your excitement will inevitably build, and you will be able to feed off that excitement to drive forward. The devil is in the detail. Don't be tempted to skimp when you get near to the finale as rushed items might bite.

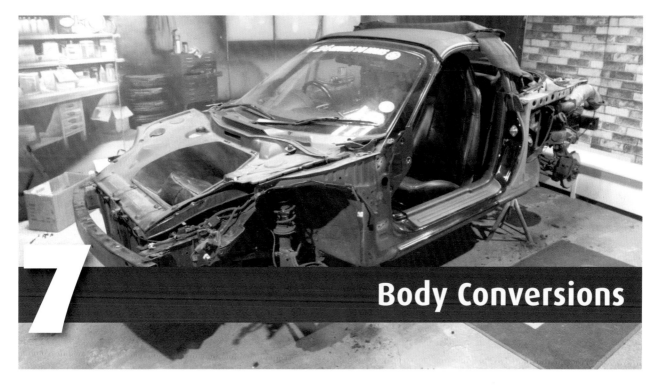

7

Body Conversions

THE BODY CONVERSION world is your oyster. There is almost an infinite number of options here. Take any car that has ever been made and change it to suit your personal preference. You could convert a Triumph Herald into a '50s special inspired race car, or a '60s VW Beetle into what appears to be a mid-engined supercar. The reality, however, is that the humble underpinnings and low power output of these two examples would produce a sheep in wolf's clothing! It's your choice. If you are not an adrenaline junkie and don't get high on speed (I'm referring to miles per hour by the way!) then you may be quite content tootling along in a car that belies its exterior. Of course, when you rev that weedy four-cylinder lump it won't sound like a V8, and when you meet a hot hatch boy racer at the traffic lights, you are going to look a right numpty as he speeds away in his 1.6 Corsa. No doubt he will wave at you with one fifth of his right hand.

Mind you, someone had the audacity to suggest that my 1.8-litre Replicar was wrong! How dare they? It has a stainless steel large bore exhaust and sounds great, but they said "bet it's got more guts than go". Actually, it pushes 172bhp out and only weighs 680kg, but the point is that, if I wanted to put a moped engine in it, it is my car (albeit in this case not a body conversion)! One guy said "you need a V8 in that", and another asked "can you fit a Hayabusa engine in one?" At the end of the day, it is all about individuality. That is why you are reading this book. The car supermarkets are full of Mundanos but I guess, like me, you are not content with what's on offer. So if it's more power per pound or bang for buck, or mpg you seek then

this is the time to draw up your battle plan. Military strategies are hopefully not required, but occasionally you may be tempted to build a blockade around your dream machine!

I did say that the choices are endless and if you take, for example, a £500 Jaguar XJS and remodel its exterior, it may well finish up with the guts to match its looks. That inline six is a heavy lump though and I prefer to adopt the tune-up options on the Mazda's bulletproof engine. Let's take this imaginary leap from mundane to magnificent one step further.

A car such as a Toyota MR2 could be considered a brilliant base on which to work your magic. Take a look at the kit car show offerings in

■ *Will your Ferrari replica attract criticism if it's only a Toyota MR2 under the skin? Who cares! It's your car, so it's your choice.*

■ *MEV X5 is a body conversion on the Mazda MX-5. Coupé body is an alternative to the donor car's roadster format.*

the Ferrari camp, and you may well see some amazing machines, closely resembling an Italian masterpiece-even though the tax disc may reveal the car's identity as being a Toyota. I mentioned beauty only being skin deep in the last chapter and some would argue in the case of body conversions, that the beauty is indeed only skin deep. Mind you, it's amazing what can be done with an exhaust pipe to generate go-faster music from the tailpipe. As I said, the choices are almost limitless. A Range Rover could become a Hummer, and a quad bike could become a road legal mini monster truck. There are only two limits to the possibilities: one is your imagination and the other is your wallet.

From a legal standpoint, provided you choose a car that is fit for purpose and does not need its structure modifying, then you can turn it into a *Mad Max* machine if you desire, provided it will still pass an MoT. If you need to cut chunks of the monocoque away, it will need to go through the IVA process and be re-registered and, if you do decide to turn a Range Rover into an American army truck, try to do it in a manner that does not call for the chassis to be modified or it too will need to be IVA'd. The same would apply if you took a Mondeo and decided to make it more sporty by chopping through the roof pillars and lowering it. This would be classed as modification to the monocoque and would also be required to be taken to your local friendly VOSA test station. Assuming

you find the limitations of a monocoque type car too restrictive upon your design flair, then you need to widen your horizons in terms of the base vehicle to include cars with the separate chassis, such as the aforementioned Range Rover.

Scimitars and TVRs can be had for realistic money these days, and feature half decent chassis that will enable you to operate unhindered by rules and regulations. The Lotus backbone chassis would also make a great donor vehicle but their prices are creeping up now and may be cost prohibitive.

Then again, if you fancy creating something like a replica Willys Jeep,

■ *Range Rover has a separate body and chassis, so you can rebody it without the need for an IVA test as long as chassis is unmodified.*

■ *MEV X5 was a Mazda MX-5 conversion. Bonnet was retained but reshaped to delete the donor's pop-up headlights.*

■ *Rear bodywork transformed the MX-5 roadster into the X5 coupé. Bodywork is wider then the Mazda's, so wheel offset was changed.*

take a look at the older Suzuki 4x4s with a ladderframe chassis that might just be right up your street. Assuming you want to limit this task in a manner that includes any major mechanical work, you may find a much more suitable option is under your nose, but you haven't spotted it yet.

A Ford Cougar has a slightly lower roof than a Mondeo and may well fit the bill for you to demonstrate your styling acumen. Areas like rear quarter glass and door handles are always a dead give away as petrolheads try to second guess your choice of base vehicle. Retaining the lighting will ensure that your disguise is weak, but retaining the doors and windows with their nice tight, draught and waterproof credentials will ensure you will be able to create a quality feel to your finished wonder.

You will find how easy it is to unbolt the massive front and rear bumper sections, and the bonnet and the boot lid or hatch. The front wings on most modern cars are removable with a few little bolts and you will soon be looking at a huge opportunity to introduce your own take on a theme. I used the Mazda MX-5 for the MEV X5 Coupé, but I felt it was too narrow and so I introduced wide rims with a zero offset enabling me to increase the overall width by over 70mm.

The wheel offset on a standard Mazda is usually 38mm, which is a measurement taken from the inside bolt face to the centre line of the rim. A zero offset wheel resulted in me increasing the width by 38mm each side. This had a major impact on the appearance and somehow made the car look lower, despite it retaining its original ride height. I then swapped the coil springs for a lowering set, which gave it that slammed to the floor look. I cheated a little bit with the bonnet initially by cutting it back and folding a new edge to create a different shape. By

doing this I lost the MX-5 look with its pop up headlights, but retained the hinges and pull cord catch that Mazda so kindly provided me with.

At the back and the front it was very easy to bolt some timber sections to what some people call the slam panels, which is where the impact absorbing bumpers are mounted. These timbers enabled me to build a pattern on the car which I carried through to the top of the original Mazda windscreen to create a fastback hardtop in place of the slashed soft top with a yellow plastic rear window.

My donor car was desperate for a coat of paint which makes it even more of a joy when removing the rusty wings and damaged bumpers and cracked light units. Even the loyal MX-5 brigade could not believe what was under that pearlescent orange coupe body. The purists were horrified! But in the words of Adam Wilkins of *Complete Kit Car* magazine: "it's an MX-5 for those who don't want an MX-5."

So take off your blinkers and take a good deep look at what's out there. There will most definitely be a vehicle on the roads that will enable you to develop your dream. This is customising to the extreme. It may be that you can build your dream motor home on the back of a Toyota HiLux pick-up truck or, if you fancy a pick-up truck, why not convert an XJS that we mentioned earlier?

Once you have converted your chosen base vehicle, you will have to contact the DVLA to correct the now-misleading information on your V5. You should also notify your insurance company, but don't worry if they rescind your policy as there are specialist insurers who will be only too happy to remove some hard earned from your pocket. You will more than likely find that your creation is now far cheaper to insure than before you set eyes on it.

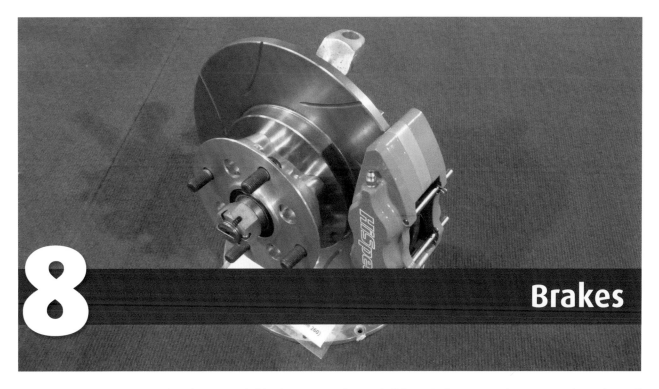

8 Brakes

WITHOUT WISHING TO state the obvious, probably the most important function of any vehicle is the ability for it to be drawn to a halt. The combination of engine, transmission, suspension and steering could all be absolutely perfect in a car that is however inherently dangerous. It's no good making it go if you can't make it stop. Very rarely do we hear bar-room banter when those competing with each other quote figures of 60mph to 0, but they will be all ears as one of them claims his latest 0-60mph dash time.

Fluid dynamics, the way brake systems work, are a fairly easy system to understand. Your brake pedal is basically used to force hydraulic fluid against a piston in a master cylinder possibly assisted by a vacuum servo. The pressure being applied will be transferred to slave cylinders operating on each wheel. These slave cylinders have a piston that moves out as the master cylinder piston is pushed in, the result being a mechanical pressure applied to the pads causing friction on the brake discs. Some brakes have shoes that rub on the inside of drums and others have multi-piston calipers that operate on pads, but the same principles apply regardless.

In simple terms, you don't get anything for nothing. So turning to the mechanical leverage of a brake pedal, it is fair to assume that a 1ft long brake pedal will need twice as much force as a 2ft long brake pedal to achieve the same stopping power. Whilst it appears therefore that the longer pedal has a mechanical advantage, the disadvantage will be that the operator's foot will have to travel twice as far.

Brake servos are bulky and can hinder the bonnet flow, but if you design a half decent brake system and your car is under 750kg it will stand on its nose if you press hard enough with or without a servo.

Turning to the pistons themselves now, there are many different bore sizes that will enable you to fine-tune the amount of fluid moved by a given pedal movement, distance or stroke. A larger bore may move the same amount of fluid as a smaller bore but in a shorter distance. In essence, if your master cylinder bore is too large for the slave cylinders that it is operating, the pedal travel will be very short, and not necessarily very efficient.

Get it wrong at the other end by replacing a single-pot caliper with a six-pot and you might find that the total surface area of the six pistons is greater than the surface area of the single-pot that it replaced. This would result in the master cylinder having to move more fluid in order for those six pistons at each wheel to move sufficiently.

Road legal cars must have a dual circuit system. This ensures that if a brake line is ruptured, the whole system is not lost – the car will still be able to stop with the braking effect on two wheels. The best way to achieve this is with a dual master cylinder, which essentially comprises two pistons in tandem, or you may consider using two master cylinders operated by a balance bar, which looks rather like a see saw, the fulcrum being your brake pedal. The advantage here is that you can select differing master cylinder bore sizes to correspond with your chosen slave cylinder sizes.

This means you could actually get it completely wrong! But it will also enable you to move more fluid for a given pedal movement to

■ *It's a good idea to renew your discs and pads during the build.*

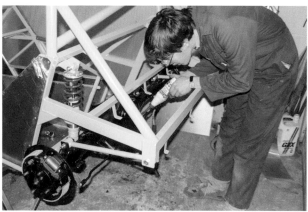

■ *Some donors will use brake drums at the rear, rather than discs.*

the front master cylinder compared to the rear. Adjustable balance bars are also available for a twin master cylinder system, and by screwing them in or out you will effectively be moving the fulcrum to give a preferential load to one piston or the other.

Provision needs to be made for storing brake fluid in a reservoir. This can take the form of a master cylinder combined unit but this may cause the height of your bonnet to increase. Alternatively, a remote reservoir can be used feeding fluid to one or both cylinders and the clutch master cylinder (assuming it is not cable). Either way, if the car is to be road legal it will need a float switch to operate a warning light on the dashboard which is usually connected via the handbrake thus creating a test mode for the warning lamp.

Turning to the brakes themselves. There are enormous differences between the material used in a road-going pad to that of a pad

designed for racing. The higher friction pads for racing tend to wear much quicker, but will be suitable for operation at much higher temperatures and less likely to suffer brake fade due to heat build up.

Now looking at the discs, it may be possible to specify varying diameter discs provided that the calipers are mounted on radial studs which will allow spacers to be introduced if you fit larger discs. Failing that you may consider cross drilled discs, that will improve heat distribution, water egress, and reduce the gas build up on the pad surface that causes brake fade.

There are also discs available that are grooved on the surface and these act to prevent glazing. Vented discs could also be an option provided you can find a matching caliper that will fit your suspension uprights. The obvious advantage being that the vented disc should keep cooler than its solid counterpart.

■ *If you're building a lightweight sports car, it may not be necessary to have the assistance of a servo.*

■ *You may not have space to re-use existing pedals, which means you could fabricate your own or source an aftermarket pedal box.*

■ *Master cylinder reservoir with proportional valve.*

To give you a basic guide and start point for a successful and efficient brake system, I use a 6:1 ratio brake pedal on the MEV Sonic7. This means that the end of the pedal is six times further away from its pivot point than the shaft that pushes the piston of the master cylinder or cylinders. It is used to operate two master cylinders via a balance bar that have a bore size of .700in for the rear calipers and .750in for the fronts. The calipers at the rear are standard single-pot Ford units and at the front I use M16 Type 4-pot calipers with 1.25in bore.

To an extent, it really is a suck it and see game, but the Sonic7 does have a relatively high brake lever ratio coupled with a fairly short pedal travel and adjustable bias. Your car will need to pass the brake tests for IVA and the inspector will need to be satisfied that the combined braking system is adequate enough to stop the gross weight of the vehicle, and that the rear brakes are less efficient than the front so that your car will not easily find itself in a doughnut situation. If you have any doubts whatsoever that your system is fit for purpose, you could take it to your local MoT station and get them to test the brakes for you. In the future you may wish to suggest to the bar room braggers that your 60mph to 0 is less than your 0-60mph time.

Electrics

WHEN MENTIONING CAR electrics to the average DIY mechanic, you may frighten the living daylights out of him. It is a subject that can frighten even the most competent builder, and a specialist area that can end in tears if you get it wrong and your car goes into melt down. It was once said that wires on cars are actually pipes full of smoke (!) and, indeed, it can appear that way if you get it wrong and they start to leak fumes.

That all sounds very negative, so please allow me to help put your mind at rest. For a starter, vehicle wiring only becomes a problem when you start to change something. If you take a wiring harness from a car, put it into your car and plug it all back in exactly as it

■ *One way to approach the wiring harness is to separate the engine loom from the car's other electrical functions.*

was, then there is absolutely no reason for it not to work, and no need for you to actually understand any of it.

When I designed the MEV Exocet, I made a point of addressing the 'scary' electrics problem. I did as I have just said, and unplugged the entire wiring loom and harness from an MX-5, labelled every single plug and socket and stuck it all back together in its new Exocet home. Do you know what? It's impossible to get it wrong. None of the plugs fit in the wrong holes, and they all fall into their rightful place apart from the earth connections.

Now here you can screw it up. I counted no fewer than seven separate important earth terminals, and all sorts of weird issues can occur if you leave even one of them off. The lights can fade, the indicators can flash rapidly and the starter motor solenoid can chatter, to name but a few miserable memories that you will have if you don't carry out a methodical transplant.

Taking another approach is to separate the engine management system from the car body functions, such as the lights and instruments. This is how I worked some sparky magic on the MEV Rocket when removing a massively complex electrical system from a Ford Focus. It became apparent that the majority of this pile of spaghetti I had just removed from the Focus was there just to confuse me. I was not interested in speaker wires, air bags, a cigarette lighter, interior lighting, or the wiper/wash facility.

Having paired back the insulating tape from this monster mass of 'pipes', I was able to eliminate what looked like 5km of cable. What

■ *If you use the entire donor loom, be sure to mark up every connection as you remove it.*

was left, however, was the engine bay wiring harness and all I needed to do was to introduce a relay for the petrol pump and another for the radiator fan. I then started from scratch and created a very basic wiring harness with separate fuses for the lighting system I required. So basic, in fact, that I found the easiest way to feed all of the light units was via a 7-core cable normally used for the backboard on a trailer. There are firms which will supply you a ready-made loom that will take care of all the rudimentary functions of a

■ *A wiring diagram will prove very useful. Draw one up once you've assembled your loom for future reference.*

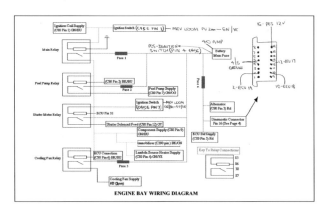

ENGINE BAY WIRING DIAGRAM

car, so you don't need to worry about, for instance, how to wire a hazard warning light switch.

If you use an aftermarket ECU, this may well simplify the engine bay wiring requirements, as they can generally be supplied with a harness and connection instructions. Mapping is sometimes an issue if you go down this ECU route, so I would strongly recommend that the ECU supplier you choose has indeed developed a suitable programme as a starting point to run your particular engine and throttle body installation.

Road legal requirements are an important consideration when designing or specifying an electrical harness or loom. A specialist loom supplier will know, for instance, that the instruments will need back lighting and that the hazards must operate with the ignition switch on or off. They should also know that a fog light switch must have a tell tale light when it is on, and also that the fog light must only be capable of illumination when the headlights are turned on. Fuses are one of the most important considerations so that if you do get it wrong, the fuses will go open circuit rather than you having to grab a fire extinguisher.

There are simple calculations to ensure that your fuse size is suitable. As an example, if you are feeding two 55-Watt headlamp bulbs with 12 volts, then in round figures you could call that total load 120 Watts divided by 12 volts which equals a minimum fuse capacity being required of 10 amps.

This equation can be used throughout the car to check for loadings on other separate circuits. For instance, four times 5-Watt front and rear marker lights (side and tail) will total 20 Watts. Round that up to

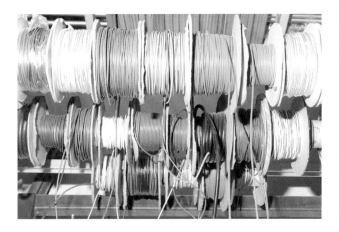

■ *You'll need a basic understanding of the theory to decide what fuses and size of cables to use where.*

■ *There are companies who can provide wiring looms for your application if you don't want to create a harness from scratch.*

24 Watts divide it by 12 volts, and the consumption is less than 2 amps.

Wire sizing is very important. You need to ensure that the weakest link in any circuit is the fuse and not the cable. Single-core PVC thin wall 1mm squared cable, for instance, is usually rated at around 16 amps. It is interesting to note, however, that standard 1mm squared cable is only rated at 8 amps, but the make up of the thin wall cable will be 32 thin strands of copper making it a high performance cable compared with the older 14 strand 8 amp cable.

In essence, 1mm cable can quite happily handle most of the apparatus on the average car with the possible exception of the starter motor solenoid and radiator fan. That may well draw 25 amps initially. If you are going to make your own loom, you really must consider investing in several rolls of different coloured cables, as if you stick 20 white cables down some convoluted tubing it could take you a month of Sundays to work out which one is supposed to go where. If you are lucky, you may find a steering column with the indicator and hazard switch gear pre-wired like a Fiesta, otherwise you will find yourself studying a tiny slip of paper that came in the box with the hazard switch.

This can be confusing. In terms of the regulations, you should also consider your switch choice. You will note from the IVA manual that clear symbols are required to make it obvious to someone unfamiliar with your car how to operate it. There are specific symbols that must illuminate for items like brake warning, hazards, indicators, side lights, fog light and main beam. Remember also that even if you are building a replica of a '60s car, if it requires IVA they are not going to allow you to have toggle switches sticking out of the dashboard without a ball on the end or a flip up toggle cover. It is worth considering from the outset that the brake pedal on your car will need to operate a switch for the stop lights. This can either be a push button on the pedal itself that switches off when the pedal is released or a hydraulic pressure switch screwed into the T-piece on one of the brake lines.

So in a nutshell, it doesn't have to be daunting at all. The individual circuits are very simple. 12 volts come from the battery positive into a suitably rated fuse, down a suitably sized cable, to an IVA friendly switch, to power up a relay for heavy loads or directly to one side of a load and the other side will be negative (ground, earth) and will return to the minus symbol on your battery. If you treat all the circuits individually it's actually very easy and quite rewarding when it all does what you would expect. If it doesn't and you can't find a fault with a simple continuity tester or a volt meter then you can either systematically work through every single connection and wire, or shout help in the direction of an auto electrician. But don't take any risks – we don't want any smoke coming out of those 'pipes'!

■ *It's a satisfying moment when instruments come to life and lights illuminate!*

IVA and Registration

THE CAR YOU build will have to be inspected and approved by the Vehicle and Operator Services Agency (VOSA) who will carry out an inspection called an Individual Vehicle Approval (IVA) test or Motorcycle Single Vehicle Approval (MSVA) test. Despite the name, the latter is also applicable to three-wheelers. When your vehicle passes, you will be issued with a IAC (Individual Approval Certificate) which will allow you to register and tax your vehicle for road use.

It is imperative that you obtain a copy of the IVA manual (or MSVA manual if appropriate) before commencing your vehicle build. If you build oblivious to the rules you will fail on some aspect of the test. The manuals, which are free to download, can be obtained by going onto the VOSA website. The exception to this rule is that if you base your car on an unmodified chassis or monocoque, in which case you will be exempt from the test. If, however, you choose to shorten a chassis or remove parts of the structure from a monocoque then it will need to go through the test procedure.

To apply for a test you will need to fill in form IVA1 and pay attention to the guidance notes for the same. In the vehicle class section you will be probably ticking the box 'amateur build', although later it may be the case that you will be ticking box 'C' as by the stage you may well be in the business of building vehicles. You may be asked to fill in an 'amateur build declaration' form and, indeed, to provide evidence that it is an amateur build, ie pictures in your domestic garage if you tick 'A' for amateur which, frankly, sounds a little condescending.

If you tick box 'L' for low volume, then you will need to provide written evidence of the number of vehicles of that type that you have manufactured and registered in a given 12-month period. If the registration officer is not happy with any of the answers you have put on the registration form, he will come back to you and agree to amend, for example, your stated maximum speed or engine output. Once the application is processed you will then receive a call from your chosen inspection station to arrange an appointment.

Inspections are carried out around the country at VOSA test stations. With careful planning, and by paying attention to the manual during the build, there should be no reason for your car to fail the test. However, if it does (and many do first time!), the inspector will give you a detailed summary of why, so you can go away and sort out the problematic items and book a retest as soon as you like (there is a time limit – if you wait too long, you'll need to start the process again from scratch).

If your vehicle fails on a minor issue (for example edge trim missing of a sharp radius) which you can correct at the test station in a short period of time, the inspector will invariably allow you to bring the vehicle back into him after you have done your alterations, thus avoiding a retest fee. For this reason, it is wise to take with you a basic tool kit, edge trim, rubber tube which you can cut and use to cover any exposed edges or nuts, cable ties, pipe P-clips and self-tapping screws. I always book a morning appointment just in case, so I can play around with any bits that need sorting in the lunch break in the hope of getting the inspector to give the car a quick glance over.

There are 20 items listed on the VOSA website that do not incur a

■ *There is a number of VOSA run IVA stations throughout the UK which you'll need to visit before your self-build can be registered for the road.*

retest fee. For instance, if your horn doesn't work or your brake warning light doesn't come on, or there are up to three interior and up to three exterior projections that need attention, or your wheel guards need moving, then there will be no retest fee. It would be inappropriate to include the list here or, for that matter, for me to include the manual itself as it is updated online on a regular basis. When viewing the manual, the most important thing to check is the issue date at the top.

Here is a list of the topics you need to pay particular attention to. This is not a complete or comprehensive list, so please satisfy yourself

■ *You'll need to build your car according to the rules outlined in the IVA manual to avoid problems when you go for the test.*

that your particular vehicle complies. There are exceptions to all of the following rules, but if you are building a car as opposed to a goods or passenger carrying vehicle then the list below should prove useful.

Anti-theft devices: This is a simple rule to comply with, as all that is required is a steering lock on the column. An alarm or immobiliser is not required but must comply if you choose to fit one.

Windscreen: A full height windscreen (if fitted) has to be manufactured to the required standard and come complete with a permanently marked E symbol. In basic terms, if the driver has to look through it to drive the vehicle then the screen must also have a means of satisfactorily demisting plus a wiper and washer system. The wipers themselves must self-park. A heated screen, if available, may negate the requirement for a warm air blower.

Seatbelts: These must be E-marked and can be a harness type or inertia reel. The mounting points will be assessed on the basis of having to withstand a load of up to two tons per person.

The height of the rear mount must be a minimum of 450mm measured from the top of a block sitting on the seat that measures 136mm by 53mm thick. To be on the safe side, you are looking at a minimum of 530mm from the top of the seat base squab. The mount must also be a minimum of 140mm from the centre line. The top of the seat itself must have a head restraint area that is a minimum of 700mm from the top of a 53mm block on the seat.

■ *Seatbelt mounting points will need to be positioned correctly.*

■ *Brakes will be tested for efficiency on a rolling road.*

Interior fittings: The bottom edge of the dashboard has to have a minimum of a 19mm radius. Anything that a 165mm sphere can contact in the 'specified zone' must have a minimum 2.5mm radius. The gear lever must have a minimum radius of 3.2mm.

Exterior projections: The same 100mm sphere will be used to check that everything it can contact externally also has a minimum 2.5mm radius, within 200mm of the edge of the vehicle. An exception here would be a shock absorber housed in between the top and bottom wishbones.

Lighting: I refer you to the IVA manual or to Chapter 5 (under the sub-heading 'light units').

Mirrors: An exterior offside mirror is required and must be able to accommodate a rectangle of 40mm high and 70mm wide. An interior rear-view mirror is also required (minimum 40mm by 80mm). If the interior mirror does not provide the required field of view then a nearside mirror must also be fitted.

Tyres: All tyres must be E-marked and also carry a speed rating, which matches or exceeds your quoted maximum speed for the vehicle.

Door catches: Top hinged doors will require an audible device to warn occupants if a door is not properly latched. All doors must have a double latch.

Protective steering: Airbags are not permitted and steering wheels must not splinter or fragment. They should be fitted with a collapsible boss and have no slots or holes in the spokes likely to catch jewellery. The spokes and securing bolts must have a minimum

2.5mm radius. The steering column itself will need to be fitted with two universal joints, offset a minimum of 10deg to restrict movement towards the driver in the event of a frontal impact.

Brakes: Brake systems are required to be a dual-circuit type and have a separate mechanical handbrake with a test light to warn of low fluid. The efficiency of the brake system will be tested on a rolling road, so inform the inspector if you have a limited slip differential. Calculations will be made to ensure the brake system is suitable for the gross weight of the vehicle.

The inspector will allow you to adjust the balance bar on site if you have fitted one, but the adjustment must be rendered inoperable once adjusted by lock wiring of components. You will also need a label securely attached on or adjacent to the adjustable bar, warning that adjustment may render the brake system unsafe for use. This is done to ensure that future drivers don't create a back-overtaking-the-front scenario.

Self-centring: The inspector will check to ensure that the steering of your car tries to self centre. If it does not it will mean that you either have insufficient castor angle or a stiff steering component.

Noise: If your exhaust emits in excess of 99dBa at two thirds maximum engine power measured at 500mm from the exhaust outlet, it will fail.

Emissions: Emissions vary depending on the vehicle age, but modern donors fitted with Lambda sensors will pass assuming the engine is running properly and fitted with the original ECU. If you can prove by showing an engine number matching a V5 that the engine is from a vehicle registered prior to August 1992, a catalytic converter is not required.

■ *Spherical testing tools check for sharp edges both inside and out.*

■ *You need space for a rear number plate. Suzuki Wagon R has two!*

■ *Chassis plate must contain 17 digits.*

Fuel pipe: In order to prove its suitability for purpose, your petrol pipe must be marked as such.

Speedometers: These must be calibrated to ensure that the vehicle speed is not shown as being less than the actual speed the vehicle is travelling at (simulated on a rolling road for the test). Inform the Inspector if you have a limited slip differential.

Number plates: Provision for a rear number plate must be made (or two in the case of the Suzuki Wagon R!).

Identification plates: Your chassis will need an identification number of no fewer than 17 digits, stamped onto the offside front, in addition to the same number being permanently etched to a plate bearing the manufacturers name and fitted to the nearside front. Weights need not be included. The letters I, O and Q are not permitted, and the letters and numbers must be at least 3.5mm high.

Radio interference: Suppression is required, but all you need to do is to show that the HT leads comply.

Wheel guards: You will need to look at the illustration to understand fully, but basically the wing must cover the rim when viewed vertically at 30deg to the front of a vertical line that intersects the hub centre and 50deg to the rear. The bottom edge of the rear of a wing must terminate a maximum of 150mm above the centreline. The use of wire wheel type hub spinners are not permitted.

Design and construction: The inspector will need to satisfy himself that the vehicle appears safe for the roads. He will look at welding to ensure that it appears satisfactory and the overall design and fitment of basically everything.

This is a get-out clause, and quite rightly. If the inspector has any concerns with regard to safety that are not covered in the rest of the manual, he may fail your vehicle if you cannot satisfy him should he become concerned about any particular area. For instance, if a monocoque were made from GRP and sub-frames were bolted to it or suspension was reliant upon its structure, he may well become concerned if stress plates are not bonded into the laminated surface.

You must read the manual yourself. With the best will in the world and in an effort to try and be helpful, people may advise you of the regulations. However, they quite often get it wrong or have only half the information. Read it yourself and, if you are not sure of what it means, talk or write to VOSA to get clarification. As you read through the above list, it will become apparent to you that the IVA inspection could have a bearing on the type of car you design. We have already discussed for example, in Chapter 1 Design Considerations, the advantages of producing a vehicle with no doors and no windscreen. There are other minor areas to address such as the requirement for a horn, instrument back lighting, control identification, hazards that operate with the ignition off, and fog lights that do not operate with the headlight off. In essence, though, there is nothing that would cause a car builder/designer extraordinaire like yourself to stumble on. You will get a Minister's Approval Certificate, and then all you have to do is jump one final very small hurdle before you drive off into the sunset in your brand spanking new motor.

REGISTRATION

The DVLA arm of the Government will help you register your car. They may at their discretion ask for a VIC (Vehicle Identification Check) so you may have to present the vehicle to them. At this stage, you are not permitted to drive it for inspection, though strangely you can drive to the IVA test if you are insured to do so. DVLA are encouraged by VOSA to accept the IAC as proof of engine/VIN instead of requesting a VIC.

If you have worked on the basis of using a donor vehicle for the major mechanical components, then once you have proven your ID, handed them a cheque for the road tax and registration fee, filled in the forms and proved that you are insured, you will hand them your donor V5 and your IAC and they will register your car with what they term as an age related plate. You will be issued with a different number plate to the one on the V5 but it will relate to the same year. If you do not produce a V5 you may well finish up with a Q-plate registration, which cannot be removed from the vehicle, so there will be no fancy private plate option for you. Many potential purchasers will generally look less favourably at a Q-plate car. This stems from the cut-and-shut era when bodged-up written-off cars were reregistered on a Q-plate.

If, however, you have used virtually all-new components for your build and can show a pile of receipts for the same, then you can apply to register your car as a new vehicle, but you are allowed one reconditioned component which could, for example, be the engine.

Either way, your newly registered car does not require an MoT for three years and, after a week or so, the bit of paper you have been desperate to see will finally land in your mail box. You may have even used your name in the 'make' and 'model' boxes on the form in which case you should quite rightly be proud to see your identity now extends to a vehicle. Turning back to the insurance aspect, it may sound weird that you need insurance before it is registered, but most specialist car insurers recognise this is necessary and allow you temporary cover for a couple of weeks based on a VIN number rather than a registration number. You may well be delighted with the attractively low fees charged for specialist vehicles, the insurers work on the basis that if you have built it you are going to try not to break it.

So that's it – job done! The moment has finally arrived. Your

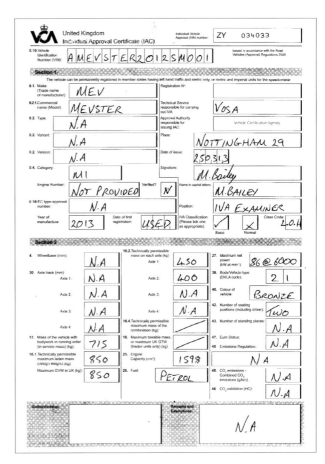

■ *When you've passed IVA, you'll receive an IAC certificate.*

dreams and all your work have finally come to fruition and there is little that is more rewarding in life than rolling in your own creation.

At first you will be nervous and you will be listening out for any suspect rattles or knocks and checking all nuts, bolts, fixtures and fittings after that initial shakedown. Confidence will continue to build the more rubber you burn. One thing is for sure, you are going to turn a lot of heads and have a lot of fun, and when you pull in to that filling station for the first time you will be very proud to tell that crowd of people that have gathered round "I built it". Your journey to that stage may well have been an emotional rollercoaster, you will have faced trials and tribulations but now you ride with pride, and this is far more exciting than any white knuckle ride.

It may be weird, it may be wonderful, but it will be special and quite possibly unique. Enjoy it and please let me see your work. I will give you a big handshake, a massive pat on the back and congratulate you on joining the exclusive club of automotive creators. Big smiles for miles!

Finance and Budgeting

FINANCING THE PROJECT is something that most certainly should not be overlooked. It would be a crying shame if you commenced work and, six months later, ran out of cash due to unforeseen costings raising their ugly heads. It will be extremely difficult, however, to pinpoint the exact amount of money required. If done on a part-time basis, these projects can often take years rather than months to complete and therefore one would assume it is possible to self-fund the development with surplus income from your 'proper' job. Nothing has to cost a fortune, however the big question is whether you have the required skill set and the available time to carry out all the elements involved in the development? It is worth considering that if this new vehicle of yours is going to sell in any numbers, the sooner it is on the market the sooner you can start receiving a return on your investment.

On that basis, it could be argued that paying others to take on some of the workload in an effort to speed up some of the development process is the way to go. A long gestation period is never going to make for a good business case, but if you intend to develop a one-off for yourself, chances are your total cost for the project need not run to the cost of a half-decent second-hand performance car. So what is the cost to develop a car from scratch? The answer is anywhere from £10,000 to £100,000. However, if you were to look at the development costs of a major manufacturer, your budget would be swallowed up just designing a dashboard for the next generation of five-door hatch.

So let us try to break down the potential associated costs that you are likely to come across. You should then aim to produce a concise document containing a list of anticipated expenditure to present as part of a business case to your local friendly bank manager. Then again, if your bottom line matches the depth of your pocket, all well and good. Either way, the document will still be useful as a reminder as to where you stand on development costs.

Let's consider a case for Jack, as in Jack of all trades. We will assume he is pretty handy on the spanners, not too bad at welding and can turn his skills to woodwork and pattern-making. It is fair to assume, therefore, that he feels he doesn't need a body stylist – "nah, I can do that" – and that he won't need to pay a structural engineer to check his chassis design, as he says "not sure about that bit so I'll make it thicker". He may work from a shed in his back garden and have access to a range of tools in his day job. Jack therefore is well positioned to create a one-off specialist car at very low costs. We assume he will be able to find the time. We should consider, however, a very important fact – professionals charge for their work because in theory they are good at it. Many people style their own body to their own satisfaction only to find that the demands of Joe Public are not met. Joe is not attracted to Jack's car body style.

It could be considered of great importance to employ the services of a structural engineer to ensure that your chassis remains in one piece. Jack, however, may consider the expense unpalatable and therefore

■ *Do you need large premises from the start?*
■ *A smaller garage may be enough to get you started.*

makes his chassis heavier than required in an effort to ensure it remains in one piece. There is a half-way house option to consider, which is employing the services of Fred the shed. Fred may have the pre-requisite skills in certain areas such as fabrication or GRP laminating but does not necessarily charge the going rate for his services as he keeps his overheads low. He probably doesn't have any product liability insurance though, so if you do come unstuck at a later date, it may be that the buck lies with you when Fred has shed his shed.

So let's look at costs which must be considered, whether you're looking to do all the design work yourself or not.

Premises: If you haven't got a garage outside your house to operate

from, or desire a little more space, you may want to rent a 1000sq ft industrial unit with a roller shutter door, a gas heater, and a good level concrete floor.

Therefore, you need to assess how long it will be until your first customer car rolls out the door to give you a return on your costs. We assume two years and, at £6.50 per square foot per year including rates, that could be considered extravagant. We haven't included heating and lighting, telephone or rubbish removal yet, but across the country rent and rates levels vary enormously. A good tip here to keep costs down is to see if you can find a farmer who will let you have a part of one of his barns for a small upfront fee, although if you invite potential customers around for a gander they may not be impressed.

Equipment: The obvious items of cost here are tools, but there are also capital costs associated with the requirement for items like an office desk, PC, a four-poster lift and a van with a car transporter trailer. You may consider none of these applicable, depending on your type of project and where you operate from, but a figure of £15,000 can very easily be spent.

Consumables: These minor items often add up considerably and you should keep a tab on them so that costs don't run away. Buying new drill bits, sanding pads, polish, welding wire and gas plus a few nuts and bolts, oil, brake fluid and clips etc, often adds up to a significant sum. You should allow a contingency figure of at least £1000 to cover these sundry items.

■ *Don't forget to budget for a desk and PC. It's not just workshop equipment that will absorb your cash during set-up.*

■ *A four-post lift will make life more easy, but it might be a luxury that can wait until you have a few sales under your belt.*

Specialist services: During your development, you may well require to have components sandblasted, powdercoated, or reconditioned. You may also need the services of an engineer for making a bespoke propshaft or modifying a differential. I would suggest as a ballpark figure you allow £1000 for these services. In addition, an amount should be allowed for items such as handbrake cables, throttle cables, brake flexi hoses, exhaust etc.

Structural engineer and/or body stylist: The services of a body stylist could cost anything from £500 to £5000. Likewise, a structural engineer could easily charge up to £5000 for designing or checking a chassis. It could be argued that specialist engineers and body stylists' fees can be well justified, as their assistance may result in a far superior product being brought to market and consequently greater potential for it to sell.

Fabrication: Given a half-decent set of drawings but a lack of

welding skills, you may wish to enlist the services of a local fabrication company to provide you with a chassis. As a very rough guide £1000 may buy you a straightforward chassis.

Pattern-maker: Assuming you have enlisted the help of a body designer/stylist, they should be able to provide you with scale drawings, or data, that can be used by a pattern-maker. Again, costs vary enormously depending whether the man uses a bag of chisels or a sophisticated computer controlled laser cutter to create a polyurethane foam buck. Anything from £5000 to £15,000 is a rough guide for a pattern also known as a buck.

Donor car: Depending on your requirement you could allow £200 for a nail up to say £10k if you require almost all new parts and no donor.

Mould construction: Once a satisfactory pattern has been made, it will need finishing to a high gloss standard, which can often be

■ *Minor items like nuts, bolts, sanding pads and welding wire quickly mount up in cost. Set aside around £1000 for these initially.*

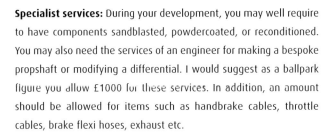

■ *Your donor car might cost anything from £200 to £10,000 depending on what's required for the car you have designed.*

■ *It's quite easy to spend £10,000 to £20,000 on mould construction. This figure can be reduced by doing more manual work yourself.*

carried out by a GRP firm who would make the moulds. You can spend anywhere between £10,000 and £20,000 quite easily. You can reduce this figure by spending time raising the finished quality of your pattern before handing it over to Mr Moulder.

GRP body: It may well be that you will use the same firm that made the moulds to take a cast from them. This is recommended, as the mould-maker will be considering ease of production when deciding how to split the moulds to release the item. To an extent it can be said that the more that is spent on the mould the less that is spent

on the casts that are taken from it. A high gloss finished mould with very neat split lines will produce a good quality car body or panels. A set for a full car without a roof would cost circa £1500 as a guide.

Windscreens: This can be an expensive item if you can't find an off-the-shelf screen without compromise to your style. The tooling and silk screen printing for a bespoke item can easily cost £3000 depending on complexity.

Auto electrician: Vehicle electrics are a specialist subject, and modern cars use complex electronics so it may well be that you will come unstuck and require expert assistance in this area. Budget £500.

■ *A full set of GRP body panels for an open-top car will cost something in the region of £1500.*

■ *Making bespoke windscreens requires specialist equipment, so you may need to budget around £3000.*

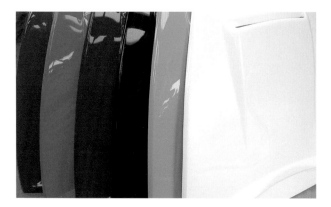

Trimmer: In order to produce a quality product, it will need to appear up to production car standards internally and externally. You should consider enlisting the services of a specialist vehicle trimmer who will make plush dashboard panels, door cards and bulkhead panels and carpeting etc. Allow £1500. Again these are figures that can vary enormously.

Accessories: Mirrors, wheels, tyres, seats, steering wheel, instruments etc can easily add up to £1500.

Tune-up kit: You may well have difficulty with some donor ECUs but, even if you don't, you may still consider a throttle body kit and after market ECU for increased performance, which can run up to £2000.

Registration fees: Once complete, unless your vehicle is based on an unmodified chassis, which severely limits your options, it will then require an IVA or MSVA test, registration, tax, and insurance. Low volume kit car insurance is excellent value so the total for this section could be as low as £1000.

Liability: We have mentioned vehicle insurance above, but one thing worth considering is product liability insurance. If you operate as a sole trader then it would be prudent to protect yourself via insurance in case of a product failure claim.

Just supposing you are found negligent in some way for supplying a vehicle or kit that then fails dramatically causing injury to its occupants, then costs awarded via a court order could be colossal. Specialist insurers, however, do offer product liability insurance cover. You may wish to write up a disclaimer for your customers to sign stating that you will not be liable as your customer accepts the goods on the basis that they are not crash-tested or stress-tested.

However, if the mud hits the fan, a judge is likely to overrule any attempt at disclaiming liability for supplying a product that is proven to be unfit for purpose. Another way to protect yourself is to establish a limited company. As the name suggests, this limits your liability as a director but would not necessarily protect you from a negligence claim. The belt-and-braces approach is a limited company with a customer disclaimer and product liability insurance.

It appears we have wandered off course a little here. However, should you require finance, a limited company may well be a route to protect you from exposure should it all come tumbling down. Be aware, though, that shrewd lenders may well ask you to sign a personal guarantee against loans to a company, in which case you're stuffed either way.

Please bear in mind the above list is a very rough guide and you

■ *You may require out-sourced help. Will you hire an auto electrician and/or a trimmer in the making of your car?*

should satisfy yourself of the actual cost by obtaining quotes where possible for all the items or specialist sub contractors involved.

Business plan: Once you're armed with this development cost document, you are well on the way to presenting a business case. If you do find yourself in need of finance, the banks will advise on specific information they are looking for in order to support your loan application. Being armed with as much information as possible is the way forward. What you need is evidence to prove that your product will sell, can be produced for the monies that you have quoted, and will show that you can make a decent profit, net of all associated costs. You will probably be asked to provide a cash flow forecast, sales targets, anticipated turnover and expected profits for year one, two and three. These figures are nearly always a complete shot in the dark, as the reality is we have absolutely no idea whether only one person will want to buy your car or if it is going to set the motoring world on fire in terms of demand.

We will need to rely on your entrepreneurial spirit to demonstrate that you have discovered a window of opportunity to create a vehicle that will sell into a niche market. I would always make it clear to the lender that you intend to cater for an existing market rather than try to create a new one.

■ *If you need finance, you'll need a business plan before a meeting with your bank manager. Make sure the figures are realistic.*

I would suggest, therefore, that when producing your business plan a certain amount of logic and reasonableness is required. Don't be tempted to say you expect to sell 5000 units in year three, as whilst this might be possible your lender is likely to be sceptical, and act on the side of the caution.

Demonstrating that you have carried out market research (covered in the marketing chapter) may help the bankers gain confidence, as you will be able to use the information that you have gleaned to convince them that you are fully aware of the bigger picture. It is unlikely that you will be providing too much information.

To substantiate the amount of initial investment that is required, if you only need to borrow £20,000 there's no point in trying to convince lenders that you'll be a multi-millionaire by year three.

Also bear in mind that there can be extra charges involved, perhaps loan set-up fees or high rates over base being charged if they consider you might be a high risk client. Getting a loan is not necessarily a goal unless the loan is available to you at competitive rates.

Your sale price: When studying the marketing chapter, which comes up next, I have included advice to ensure your product is competitively priced in the marketplace. The bottom line needs to be a figure that you are comfortable with, but it is very easy to assume a chosen margin without considering all of the facts.

A business adviser would have you compile lists of costs including ink for your printer, replacing the worn out carpet under your office

chair, buying toilet rolls, hand towels, and earning a few extra quid from scrap. The bean-counters will also insert a figure into your end of year accounts for depreciation on capital expenditure, this can offset tax on profit. Obviously there are a considerable number of cost items to consider, including your accountant's fees and any holiday pay, and even paying staff when they are off sick. Taking this route to find your true overheads has to be considered the best approach, your profit margin can then be finely tuned enabling you to possibly be more competitive or, for that matter, more profitable than you had previously assumed.

My approach has always been to ignore the fact that a calculated margin could be as low as a 30 per cent mark-up on cost and instead consider the cost of the item you are selling. Let us consider a GRP body that cost you £1000 from a sub-contractor, added to the materials and labour costs of in-house fabrication of the rest of a vehicle's components. If the total were, say, £2000 for argument's sake, I would aim to double it and retail at £4000 plus VAT. This may seem a lackadaisical approach, it may also be considered that 100 per cent is a ridiculously high margin but, if you only sell one a month, then your gross profit is only £24,000 a year.

One thing we have not entered into the equation is development costs, and if you have spent £100,000 up front and expect, quite rightly, a return on that of say 20 per cent, then your £100,000 would need to be paid back into your hot sticky little hands within a five-year period. So 100 per cent divided by five years equals 20 per cent per year. Let us assume, therefore, that you are going to sell one a month for five years. That will be a total of 60 units and £100,000 divided by 60 will result in you needing to add £1666.66 to your retail price. You need to ask yourself if this is realistically possible and juggle the figures until you are comfortable.

As an aside, there is a possible VAT implication that may impact upon your retail price. Once you are up and running and your annual turnover exceeds the VAT threshold limit, you will need to charge VAT on all sales. The advantage is that once you are registered for VAT you can claim VAT back on almost everything you buy, but in very basic terms your retail price to a customer will need to increase if you are to maintain your margin.

So let's stop and have a reality check for a moment. Personally, I do not

■ *Calculate your sale price carefully according not only to what rivals charge but also your own costs and overheads.*

recognise the meaning of the word 'no' and do not respond well to negativity. In this book, however, it may be considered irrational to encourage you, the reader, to follow my obstinate nature. My advice to you, therefore, is to proceed with caution and assess potential losses if your vehicle fails. You do not want to be locked into a finance package with a personal guarantee resulting in an extra mortgage for 20 years. What you should do is control your exposure to ensure that if it all comes tumbling down the financial implications do not change your lifestyle. One way to limit your exposure is to grow slowly, and not try to dominate the world of specialist cars in year two.

Rapid expansion is often cited as a cause for failure. If through lack of development a fault occurs and the Vehicle Safety Branch of VOSA demand a recall then you could well be between a rock and a hard place if you have started moving a lot of units out the door. You do need to work very closely with your customers, especially in the initial stages by responding promptly to feedback and ensuring that those early guinea pigs are satisfied.

You need to be clear in your own mind whether this project was initiated with the aim of giving yourself the feel-good factor. Alternatively, do you see pound signs when you blink as you are motivated by money? If I can be open and honest for just one moment... if financial gain was the key for me, I would be looking to use my skills in other industries.

Marketing

ONCE YOU HAVE decided to invest your time and money into creating your own vehicle and come out the other end proudly driving it around, you may find people start asking you "where can I get one of those?" or "how much did it cost?". This may lead you to think that perhaps you could make it a viable proposition to re-create your chassis and body and associated parts to re-sell a car kit to others. If you are thinking along these lines it may well affect the processes you employ when building your own first car. At the end of the day, you must build a car that you personally love and if others happen to as well, that's a bonus.

■ *If you're marketing a replica of a 1950s sports car, then your target market will mostly be an age group who remembers the original.*

In my experience, the market for specialist cars has been shifting and continues to shift. It absolutely had to in order to survive. For many years all that could be seen at kit car shows were Lotus Seven look-alikes and Cobras and the halls were populated with men heading towards retirement age. I believe that everybody involved knew a shake up was desperately needed to attract some young blood; more modern kits, donor cars that weren't nearing extinction, reliable back-up from the manufacturers and great owners' groups. These are some of the reasons I was inspired to make my more recent creations appeal to a much wider and younger market, and it has paid off.

Youngsters love a modern sleek design, they love speed, and they love a car that can outperform a production car and is a fraction of the cost. Moving on to your desired product, we must try to define the boundaries of your likely market. Age and financial status of your potential customer will need serious consideration so let's see where you and your car may fit in.

Before any product is developed, first of all the market must be analysed to determine whether there is potential for sales success within the anticipated target audience. Demographics play a huge part in this process in an effort to calculate rather than guess your market (demographics is a term used to describe information based on statistical characteristics of a population). Calculations based on this information are required to assess the potential sales of virtually any consumer product, be it a cappuccino machine or a car.

No clear figures exist to determine the average specialist car buyer,

■ *The MEV Exocet has typically attracted a younger buyer. Many are in their 20s, and for some it's their first kit car build. Will Parry built his diesel powered Rocket when he was 18.*

but as an indication, the majority of current kit car offerings are '60s replicas and so it is safe to assume that the majority of buyers are aged 50-plus. These guys are drawn in due to their childhood memories, the older ones will remember a Lotus Seven being used in the television program *The Prisoner*. That said there are plenty of younger people who love classics. Take the VW camper for example, and let's not forget the surge of new production cars that are themed on '60s creations such as the Fiat 500 and the Mini.

It has been said that Mr Average supposedly has a Mondeo and 2.2 children, and with a mid-life crisis looming, he may well be looking to venture into something more exciting than watching *Coronation Street*. We can assume also that our industry thrives on surplus income that has become spare now the 2.2 kids have flown the nest. It could be argued that the '60s replicas market is well catered for with an array of kit cars to suit varying taste, ability to build and size of pocket, so with Mondeo man possibly out of the equation let us turn our attention to the PlayStation generation.

An 18-year old may well be drawn to an exoskeletal kit car such as the MEV Rocket, Mevabusa or Exocet. The question is, does he have enough cash, the required skill level, the tools, a garage and the time? The obvious point here is that younger potential buyers are less likely to have as much disposable income and mechanical experience as the older purchaser who may well have a garage, or even a double garage at the side of his house. We must remember, however, that some 18-year olds have built kit cars with a bag of spanners under a tarpaulin at the side of their mum's houses!

Creating a contemporary car that is to be manufactured in low volume or sold as a kit may be a way to reach a wide audience rather than direct a new product at a particular market sector such as a 45-year old ex biker, an 18-year old hot hatch driver, or a bored retired 65-year old.

Let's consider a direct comparison of the product you intend to create. For instance, the MEV Exocet. This kit car has proven to be a major success story from day one, with over 300 kits having been sold in just over two years. Market analysis for this particular product has shown that the average age of the buyer is 28 and it is therefore not considered a major threat to the rest of the industry as new purchasers are being attracted rather than levered away from other manufacturers. More to the point, it appears that the majority of Exocet builders have not built a kit car before and are drawn in as the task looks do-able. Interestingly, looking at the crowds at the 2012 Stoneleigh kit car show, it appeared the average age was 40 to 60. This point may be totally irrelevant if you are planning to produce a low volume turnkey car rather than a kit, but coming back to the disposable income point it would be quite logical to assume that 40 to 60-year olds are more likely to have enough spare cash to be buying expensive toys than 18-year olds. So to build up a picture of the type of customer you wish to aim your product at, your market research should extend to ascertain the following:

1 What age group is your product likely to appeal to?

2 Is the potential purchaser male or female?

3 Is there a likelihood that those in certain occupations are more likely than others to find your product of interest?

4 What level of income do you expect the potential customer to be earning?

5 What kind of lifestyle does the potential customer have?

6 What range of hobbies and interests are potential customers likely to have?

7 Which part of the world do you expect them to live in predominantly? For instance, an open top car is more likely to appeal to those nearer the equator!

8 What is the total value of the car or cars they currently own?

9 What product similar to your own are they currently driving, building or own?

10 Are they likely to require finance for their purchase?

The above considerations will help you fine-tune a marketing plan, also known as a marketing strategy or a marketing initiative. It may also include market research in the form of a customer survey. If you are bold enough, you could pitch yourself in the car park at a petrolhead gathering with a clipboard, and ask passers by for one minute of their time. Some will be only too glad to help but, in my experience, some can be discourteous! Questions similar to those above may reveal the answers that you are looking for. Once you get the ball rolling, customer surveys will become much easier and can be done online once you have built up a customer database.

Your strategy should include the following elements:

1 General marketing

2 Online marketing

3 Advertising

4 Branding

5 Advertising literature

6 Overseas advertising

7 Product placement in the market

8 Exhibiting at shows

9 Racing

10 Competitor awareness

11 Pricing

12 Editorial content

13 Database

1. General marketing would include exposure of your products in a manner that portrays an image in which a potential customer may feel comfortable. This is not just about showing your car to the local car club fraternity, it's more about showing you and your business in the right light. For instance, we must consider that you only get one chance at a first impression, and when a customer arrives at your premises, will they see good signage on the side of the building, the

firm's van outside (that is not a nail, but one that is used as a marketing tool with appropriate graphics)?

When they step in to your workshop or showroom...

· Will it be clean and tidy, and well laid out?

· Will you greet them with a cup of tea or coffee?

· Will you welcome them with a smile and a handshake?

· Will you hand them a quality leaflet?

· Will you be wearing a smart sweatshirt with the company logo embroidered on it?

The purchasing procedure must be an enjoyable and easy experience for your customer. To make it fun you should take them for a spin in your demo car. Don't be tempted to frighten them to death or risk injury by pushing too hard in an effort to impress with your car's ability.

The chances are that a spirited drive with the odd hard push around a safe turn will be sufficient to close a deal. If you see your passenger going for an imaginary brake pedal you may have done enough but going one step further may give the impression that you, the salesman, are reckless.

The old trick is to attach a £5 note to the dashboard and let your passenger know that they can have it if they can grab it as you move

■ *Your workshop/showroom needn't be huge, but you should strive to make a good impression by keeping it clean and tidy.*

away. Try this with a friend first or it could get expensive. Provided you are certain that it is safe to do so, drop the clutch at high rpm and in most cars they will not get your fiver! So that is the fun part dealt with and now, in order for you to have a chance of closing the deal whilst the iron is hot, you need everything in place. A credit card facility, finance forms (assuming you are licensed to offer credit), bank transfer details, a receipt book for cash, and a clear order form with all options and details laid out in a concise manner.

2. Turning to online marketing, it is desperately important these days that a decent website is created to give the right impression. We are not talking about a DIY free website but a half decent one that doesn't need to cost more than a few hundred pounds. It needs to be user friendly, interactive if possible and feature good quality images and an easy-to-follow menu. The user journey on your site is an important consideration.

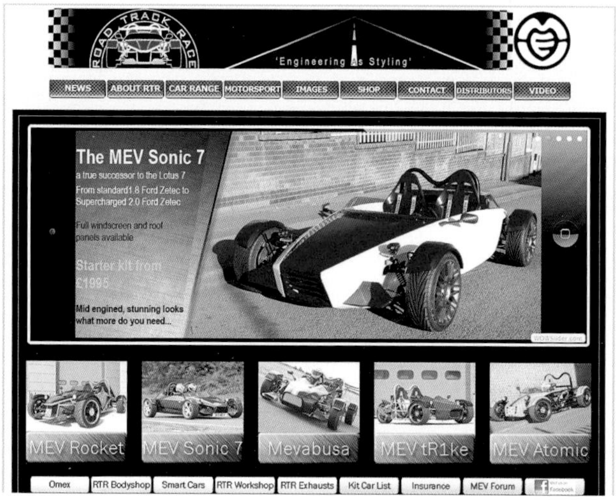

■ *It's generally considered that you need a professional looking website to create a good impression.*

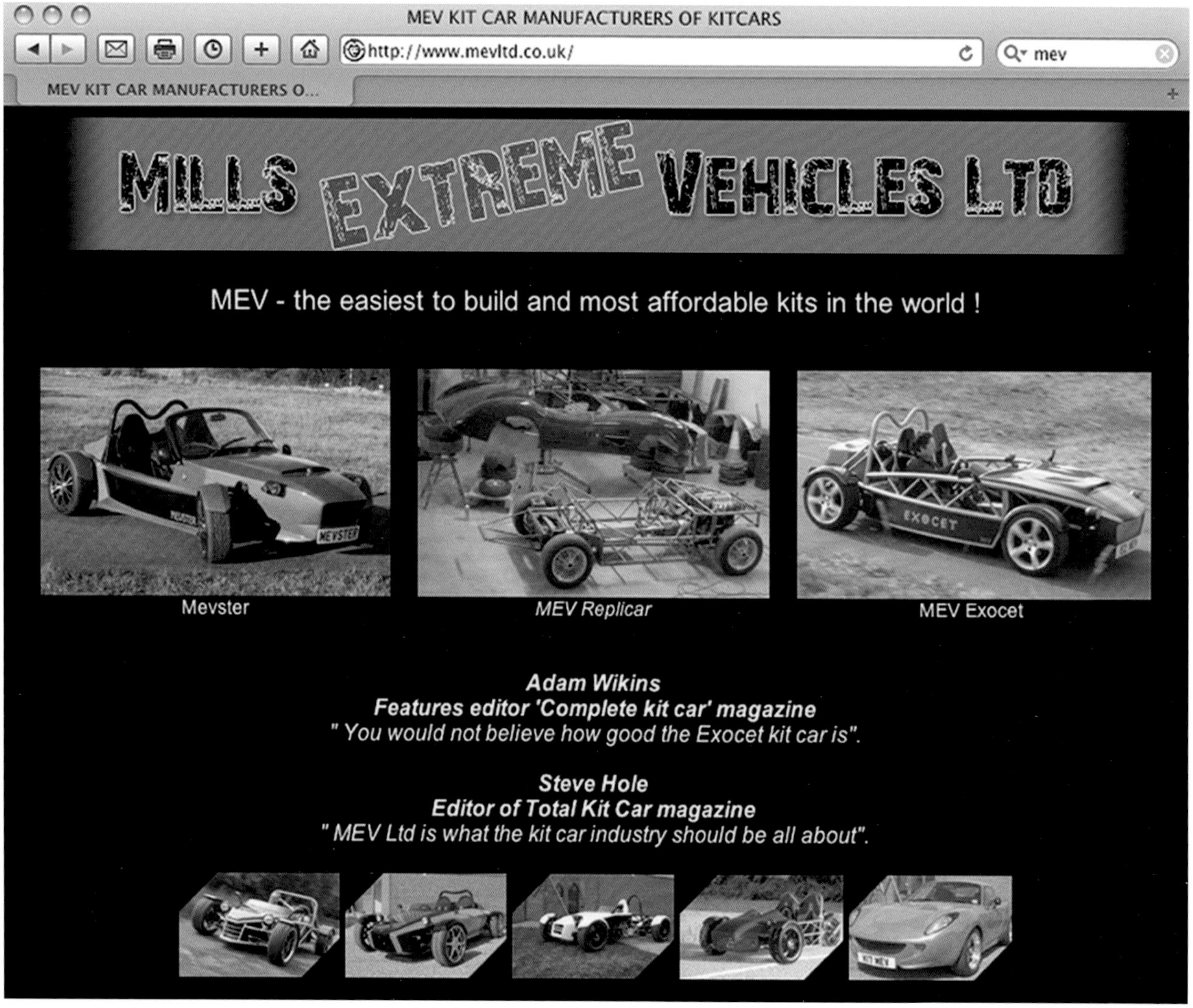

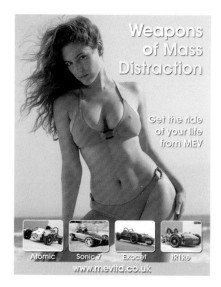

■ *Come up with advertising campaigns which convey an interesting message and highlight your car's unique points.*

Your web designer should be able to advise on elements that you may not understand, such as search engine optimisation, links to social media, such as Twitter and Facebook, and links to other petrolheaded related sites who should, if asked, repay you with a link to your site from theirs. It looks to me like this is probably going to be your most important marketing tool as you will be able to use it to encourage people to look at what you have on offer by visiting various forums, and posting in a manner that always finishes up with your product or company name or website link at the bottom. You will be marketing your marketing itself by promoting visits to your site. Forum moderators often strictly control advertising, but a tip here is to get one of your mates to start a thread and then for you to go on and reply without it being obvious that you are selling – ie, don't say your car is the best thing since sliced bread and butter, don't mention the price, and don't say it's better than someone else's comparable product. Make friends on the forums, creep if you have to but remember they will be there to help you later if somebody has a dig or you need any help getting people discussing your car.

3. Coming up with an advertising ploy for the internet and getting it to go viral is a difficult one to pull off. A YouTube clip with a flying car trick might work. In the case of the MEV Replicar, I circulated everybody and anybody informing them that whilst the original Aston Martin was now up for sale for £20 million, they may be interested in a replica kit for £5000. Now that attracted some attention and got the web statistics moving!

When it comes to advertising, you need to take a serious look at your budget here. A tiny advert in a magazine may well be cheap but is anyone actually going to spot it? To me the best adverts are those with a headline that should catch the reader's attention or inspire curiosity.

If for instance, your car looks like it may have a £30,000 price tag, you may grab attention by saying "from only £5000" or whatever your minimum starting price point is. It's always best to keep adverts uncluttered. The minimum of information is all that is required as what you are trying to do is to get the reader to click onto your site. Not much point in taking up valuable space by printing your email address, telephone number and address, they will find all this info on your site.

Very few people seem to make telephone enquiries, the vast majority of enquiries we receive at MEV HQ are via email. The magazines that you intend to advertise in generally offer a service, often free, to design an advert for you once you have provided them with a decent photograph and the message you wish to get across.

■ *Spend some time getting your PR photographs just right.*

■ *The author no longer thinks the MEV logo is as good as it could be, but it's now so well known it would be a mistake to change it.*

Skype is not my favourite means of communication as it can take up a lot more of my time than an email that can be answered at your convenience. I should point out that, in my experience, questions and answers via email lead to further questions and answers so it will help to save time if you compile a list of frequently asked questions (FAQs) for your website, and also have them available in your email drafts folder enabling you to click and paste a longer answer than is possibly required.

You should ask the magazine's advertising sales team to provide you with statistics for their readership. These are often numbers that can be taken with a pinch of salt. However, they will give you an idea of the potential audience. If, for instance, the publication you are about to advertise in informs you that they have 10,000 subscribers and in addition sell 2000 per issue through retailers then it may be worth considering that you don't need to advertise every month, or you will be paying to put the same message before the same 10,000 people every month. When you have made lists of the publications that are likely to be read by your target audience, it will be interesting to note the huge difference in advertising rates from one publication to another. Primarily, this is due to the fact that the higher rates are charged by magazines with higher readership. This of course is what you would expect, but if you are selling a kit car your money would be better spent in a kit car magazine than in a general motoring publication that may have ten times the readership, charge ten times as much for an advert, but the result may be that only one tenth of their readership is actually interested in kit cars.

Likewise, if you are only selling turnkey cars, then there will be a limit to how many kit car magazine readers will be interested in your product.

The most important point to remember with advertising is monitoring. Ask every person who telephones or emails where they found you. Keep a record of their contact details in your customer database list. Remember to keep your adverts fresh, do not just bang the same advert in each month. Maintain a certain style but try to re-invent it once it has been printed.

Regular adverts always seem to work better than a one hit campaign. My approach has always been to favour four bi-monthly quarter page ads rather than one page for one issue, unless your budget stretches to four full pages. Spreading out the exposure with four small, rather than one large, advert serves as a regular reminder to readers over four issues at a similar cost. Spend some time getting the pictures of your car for an advert just right.

4. Branding can play an important role in the overall image portrayed by your company or business. As an example, when you vacuum your carpet in the lounge most of us do it with what we call a Hoover even though, in my case, we don't have a Hoover but we do have a Dyson. Dyson is a big brand but Hoover were there first and that is a tough cookie to crack.

Careful consideration is required before creating a logo. It may be helpful to consider your brand in terms of how easy it is to remember, and therefore the use of your initials may not work too well. An arrangement of initials with no vowels will result in you expecting your customers to remember a random selection of letters. My company is Mills Extreme Vehicles Ltd, which is quite a mouthful, but we are known as MEV, not M.E.V. so we have a word that can be spoken with a vowel in the middle. This facilitates those who read it to enter it into their memory bank as a single hit word. That said, BMW don't seem to have a problem with us remembering their random three letters, but most people have no idea that it stands for Bayerische Motoren Werk.

I designed the MEV logo many years ago and was keen to make something that was round. We sell cars and it seemed logical to have a round logo that would fit neatly on wheel centres but, in hindsight, when you look at the MEV logo, most people don't realise that the letter M and E and V are actually what it comprises. I believe it would be a grave mistake to change it now though as so many people have begun to recognise it. So my advice is that unless you're 100 per cent satisfied that your talents stretch to artistic graphic design, then you may want to ask your leaflet printer or sign-maker to come up with a few ideas.

5. It is important to be able to hand a glossy booklet or even a simple colour flyer to your potential customers. When you turn up at a filling station in your pride and joy, you will be asked on many many occasions what it is that you are driving. A perfect opportunity to thrust a leaflet into their palm and, when you have finished chatting, remind them to visit your website.

One problem with leaflets is that, when you have had 5000 printed, you may well find you still have 4000 of them two years later, by which time it could all do with refreshing. In that two-year period you may well have modified the car, improved it or just painted it. You may have a version with different wheels, or other optional extras.

These will all make the leaflet appear dated, but you can guarantee that if you print your price on 5000 leaflets that this may well turn out to be the one reason they all need sticking in the recycling bin. As with adverts, I mentioned above that it is not necessary to include too much information. The same applies to leaflets. It's far better to use them to dangle a carrot and entice the recipient to visit your website. When you do finish up with a price change or a better picture due to the sun catching your car just right,

then your website can be updated with a click, but your leaflets may as well be etched in stone.

6. In terms of overseas advertising, I would recommend that you stick strictly to online options. It is likely that you have no idea of how well distributed overseas magazines are compared to the UK, where all you need to do is visit a WHSmith to see the publications that might meet your advertising requirements. Forums are probably the cheapest way to gain overseas exposure, but rather than just posting comments on various threads you may well find that an advert on a busy forum could pay big dividends. You should compare forums statistics, member numbers and frequency of use and then ask the administrators for the cost of a banner type advert.

Try a suck-it-and-see approach for three months. Allow me to repeat myself: the most important thing with advertising is

■ *At shows, some companies may take your car onto their stand to add interest to their own wares.*

monitoring. Remember to ask every person who telephones or emails where they first heard of you.

It will be helpful to understand your potential customers situation. In most of Europe, as an example, it is almost impossible to register a new car for the roads unless it is type approved. Most European one-off car builders bring them to Blighty for testing and registration to get around their restrictive legislation.

Australia is also a difficult country. They have a strict test procedure which prohibits cars from their roads unless they are capable of withstanding very high torsional rigidity loads. The MEV Rocket, however, managed to achieve the goal and is now sold via an agent in Oz, although they did have to fit a clumsy looking nose cone to it (the reason given was to protect pedestrians).

The USA is massive compared to the UK but the specialist car market is relatively small. The 50 different states are like 50 separate countries and car legislation varies enormously. One thing they all have in common, however, is the language barrier.

It has been said that the UK and the USA are separated by 4000 miles and a common language. Be prepared to adjust your terminology with words like hood, trunk, motor, gas, fender, and find out what four on the floor means. Huge opportunities exist in the States, UK labour rates are now competitive enough to allow export costs to be absorbed in a US retail price.

■ *At shows, remember you're there to sell. Draw people in and spend an appropriate amount of time with each potential customer.*

■ *If you gain good results, racing can add a halo effect to your brand. It's a potentially expensive form of advertising.*

7. You may find opportunities to get your vehicle seen at no cost to yourself. When you walk around car shows, you may well see companies selling trailers or four post lifts and, in order to brighten their exhibition space, they often seek to display a smart vehicle of an unusual nature that will enhance their own product. To my mind, the exhibitor selling a multitude of accessories for cars would create a much more attractive environment if all his mirrors, seats, lights, wheels and other cling-ons were fitted to a car that's on his display stand. This approach may well bring his products to life. In an ideal world placing

your product in a glamorous situation would often appear to add perceived value to the image of your car. Imagine if you were lucky enough to get a photo opportunity with a celebrity. My guess is that TV and football stars are given some pretty hefty incentives by the major car companies in order to get them in their seats.

Let's face it, if your car is good enough for Daniel Craig or David Beckham then it must be good enough for millions of others. I used to have a picture of a Lewis Hamilton look-alike sitting in a MEV Sonic7. I never said it was a picture of the man himself but it did look very convincing. I call that cheating!

8. Exhibiting at shows is considered extremely important. The shows need to be right for your product, however, in the same way as you must choose the right magazine to place your adverts. I have exhibited at major car shows and had 20,000 to 100,000 people walk past over a long weekend, only to find little change in traffic according to my website statistics and a result of nil point in terms of sales numbers. On the other hand, I have in the past taken a Sunday drive to a local car club gathering and made sales. It's a

difficult one to pinpoint, but it's best not to assume that every petrolhead is interested in every car.

Quite a lot of the car shows, like the bigger ones at the NEC in Birmingham, attract like-minded people to view and not necessarily buy. Again, the costs of these shows can vary considerably. I personally find it far more cost effective to exhibit at the smaller shows where fees can be as low as £150 and generate half a dozen sales compared to the larger shows that can cost £5000 that don't quite attract the exact profiled customer that I had previously identified as my target.

Image is of paramount importance at shows. Your audience has paid to see your car in the best possible light. It needs to look its best, so do you and so does your stand space. Remember, if you were there exhibiting for two days a cost of say £500, then every person that walks past may have cost you 10p or more.

Don't let them pass without asking them if you can help or offering them a leaflet, and try not to spend more than a few minutes with each customer. Your time is valuable and needs managing.

One other point is to continually remind yourself that you are there to sell. Don't let the conversation stray to nice a little chat about the guy's old Cortina. Be polite and move on. Ask yourself what the most frequently asked question I receive at shows is? You may expect it to be 'how much?', 'how fast?' or 'how easy is it to build?' Actually, the most common question is 'how many have you sold?' I will let you draw your own conclusion as to why that is the case.

9. Racing can be an expensive hobby. However, in the case of the MEV MX150R (the race version of the Exocet) we were able to

■ *If you give a magazine an 'exclusive' or 'first drive', it's more likely your car will make it to the front cover.*

introduce a comparatively very low cost racing car, and when non-race drivers see a car winning they may be tempted to buy one or, if they already have one, get the feel-good factor – as indeed does the manufacturer. When your car is sitting on the grid and the commentator is describing what it is and how much it is you have just reached hundreds, sometimes thousands, of potential customers who perhaps would not have discovered your car otherwise.

10. Competitor awareness can be considered very important, and it may well be very helpful for you to look at how your competitors operate in terms of online marketing, the shows they exhibit at, and in what way it could be considered that their product is of a higher spec or quality or, for that matter, inferior to what you have to offer.

When talking to customers, however, you should always remain professional in order to portray the right image. You should play on your strengths rather than dare to diss a competitor as that approach may well set alarm bells ringing in the ears of that person who may assume you feel threatened by your competitor. In actual fact the more you mention a competitor's name, the more your potential customers are likely to remember it.

11. When considering pricing, if your car is directly comparable to another then the pricing should also be directly comparable; lower if

■ *Make sure your owners have fun by making the club a fun, active group to be part of. This photo is from an event at the MEV factory.*

you want to be competitive or higher if it's obvious that yours is of a higher quality. If your competitor has a strong brand, image, or reputation then you will be struggling to sell against them unless you can offer better value, or a better product in terms of performance perhaps.

12. Turning to magazine editorial content, you should hold the journalist in the highest regard. They can be invaluable as they tend to be very experienced, able to advise and are very helpful. Once a journalist is invited to cover your car, you need to be prepared. The car they are about to test needs to be as good as it can get. The last thing you need is for it to run out of fuel, boil over, or have an irritating rattle. You need to prepare yourself, too. They will ask all sorts of questions, but do not be pushed for an answer if you are not sure. Ask whether it is OK to get back to them on a few points. That will buy some time to think. A good magazine article can pay enormous dividends, but a bad one can kill your product if it does not meet expectations. Someone once said that all publicity is good publicity. I do not subscribe to that theory as, in fact, a negative comment written by an independent specialist may well be the point that sticks in the mind of what could have been your customer.

Ask the journalist before they leave if they have any concerns or negative points they have come across. Ask if you can then address these points. Make an excuse, or ask them to include reference to the test car being a prototype that will be improved prior to production. If, for instance, the test drive reveals poor brakes or slow steering, then you can add that upgrade pads and a quick rack are available

in the options list. So do have that price information available if you can pre-empt what may be raised as an issue.

A magazine front cover will add enormously to your free exposure, but you may need to offer a 'first drive' or 'exclusivity' to your chosen magazine before being granted this privilege. You should be fair and open with all the magazines. They will be familiar with the tactics often played by manufacturers trying to gain free publicity, and remember that when Jaguar or Ford release a new car it appears on the cover of all the appropriate publications.

The mistake is often made by manufacturers of showing a car before it is ready. Remember the phrase you only get one chance at a first impression. I have used this one already. It is all very exciting when your blood sweat and tears culminate in a finished product, but it needs to be completely finished before you open yourself up to potential criticism.

You should not necessarily consider the offer of front page exposure to be a favour. Magazine editors are always on the lookout for new ways to increase readership, and it goes without saying that your car may well be a magnet that sells the magazine, so it can be a two-way street. No doubt you will be asked to advertise in a magazine that has included a feature of your car.

If you feel it may be beneficial then go for it, but my advice is to wait. First of all, you can use the editorial as a way to measure response from readers. This will give you a good indication of the anticipated enquiries that could be generated from an advert in the same publication. If no-one telephones or emails saying (don't forget to ask how they heard about you) "I saw you in magazine xyz", then it may be prudent to spend your money elsewhere. One would hope that you do receive increased website traffic and enquiries following editorial coverage, but I suggest that an advert in the same issue as the piece on your car is possibly wasted. An advert in the following issue will serve as a reminder to the readers of what you have to offer.

13. Create a database by retaining contact information for everyone who has been in touch with you via email, telephone or letter. This list may also include specialist component suppliers, journalists, forums, car clubs and exhibition organisers. This will prove a valuable marketing tool at a later stage. One click will enable you to send a news release or special offer to all those people who may or may not be interested, but if your email shot is hard hitting it may just get tongues wagging, and the cost to you is a little bit of time and no money.

CONCLUSION

It is difficult to imagine a situation where your marketing efforts could be considered excessive and so the main point to remember is cost effectiveness. Attending a show, for instance, has serious cost implications; fuel, accommodation, leaflets, expenses, stand hire, etc. Some show organisers will charge you extra for carpets and a backdrop, all of them seem to charge extra for a power point. It is therefore very easy to spend £1000 over a weekend and sell nothing, but don't expect too much too soon from your marketing efforts.

It may be year two or year three when your prospect returns to place an order, by which time he will have confidence that you are not a fly-by-night and has had time to get his own house in order prior to placing his order. Just sit tight and if your product, pricing and attitude all suit the customer's palette you can sit and watch your order book grow, but don't expect the phone to ring off the hook on day one.

As a word of advice, do not lose sight of the fact that you aim for all of your customers to become close friends, so if they bring a minor issue to your attention, regardless of who is to blame, you should throw a few quid at the issue to nip it in the bud.

It can be the case that if you give an inch they will take a mile, but remember that your customer/friend will have a bunch of leaflets stuck under his seat and he will act as an independent, nothing-to-gain, sales advocate when he visits his filling station. The more you sell, the more free adverts there will be travelling around the roads helping to ensure that your initial investment slowly trickles back into your pocket. Make your owners' group a fun place to be, your best advert is your customers having fun in your cars.

So turning back to the start of this chapter where I said "once you have decided to invest your time and money", this is the point of no return, but if you feel like you're jumping in the deep end then you need to either study all the Chapters involved in this book more precisely or throw caution to the wind and get going.

Once you have started you will gain more confidence as your vision starts to materialise. Getting your vision through to the marketing stage is one giant leap for you to take, but once you land you will deserve a gold medal. You may need to present this medal to yourself however, as it is unlikely anyone else will do it for you. Your real reward, the point at which you may even feel emotional, is when your first customer signs on the dotted line.

DESIGN

If you feel that your design is so earth shatteringly wonderful that it ought to be protected from copying, then you may seek to register

your design via the Government's Intellectual Property Office.

It is worth consideration, however, that others may have gone before you and protected their designs, so if you are planning to build a replica, you would be well advised to ensure that the design is not registered, and therefore protected. There is a search facility on the IPO website. The protection expires 25 years after a design was registered, or after five years if the renewal fees are not paid. Some, however, have created case law by claiming their product is in some way 10 per cent different to a registered design and have been let off the hook. However, other cases have resulted in small companies being crushed by the big boys who seek to protect their designs, and have been known to win very weak cases due to their financial clout. A court case should be avoided at all costs and, in my experience, unless you have a concrete case and are 100 per cent likely to win back your costs, then the sensible thing to do is move on whether you like it or not.

Bear in mind that even if a design is not registered there is 'design right' which offers UK protection for 10 years from when a design was put to market, or 15 years from when a design was created. A design cannot be registered once it has been made public for over a year.

PATENTS

It is worth considering that when your brain starts to go into

■ *If your idea could be termed an invention, you can seek to protect your design with a patent.*

■ *If you're planning to build a replica, make sure the design isn't registered. There's a search facility on the government's IPO website.*

overdrive, it is quite conceivable that your mind could envisage what is termed as an invention. If you suspect that this mechanical device or system of yours has not been utilised before, you should consider carrying out a patent search on the appropriate Government website.

If you are in luck, it may be an idea to apply to register the patent. This is a fairly complex procedure. However, I have always applied for a patent myself rather than using what can turn out to be a very expensive agent. The Intellectual Property Office (IPO) staff will give you help and should you not satisfy the application criteria they may well ask you for more information. If your application is successful you will receive a certificate which may prove to be a nice little earner at some point in the future if someone asks permission to use your invention under a licence agreement.

TRADEMARKS

The Government IPO website is an excellent tool allowing you to apply online and search existing trademarks as well as gaining useful advice on making applications. You can seek to protect a trademark, which could be your company logo (known as a 'device') or a made up word if you wish it to remain exclusive. There are separate classes for automotive registrations... that is why we can buy a Wimpy burger or have a firm with the same name build us a house. Different classes.

The registration process does not have to be expensive if you do it yourself. I have successfully registered trademarks for Europe including Exocet, Battmobile (sic), Replicar and others. The reason I mention these three is because I was surprised no one had got there before me. Exocet was registered as a missile allowing me to register it under 'vehicles'.

Useful Contacts

After you've designed your car, you'll need to construct it. This list includes many suppliers you'll find useful along the way.

BRAKE PARTS (discs/calipers/pads)

AP Racing T: 024 7663 9595. W: www.apracing.com

EBC Brakes W: www.ebcbrakes.com

Ferodo W: www.ferodo.co.uk

HiSpec Motorsport T: 01322 286850. W: www.hispecbrake.co.uk

Mintex W: www.mintex.co.uk

MNR T: 01423 780196. W: www.mnrltd.co.uk

Pagid W: www.pagid.com

Rally Design (Wilwood) T: 01227 792792. W: www.rallydesign.co.uk

CARBURETTOR/INJECTION SERVICES/ENGINE MANAGEMENT

DanST Engineering T: 07921 168507. W: www.danstengineering.co.uk

Omex Technology T: 01242 26065. W: www.omextechnology.co.uk

Race Technology T: 01773 537620. W: race-technology.com

Webcon T: 01932 787100. W: www.webcon.co.uk

COOLING SUPPLIERS (RADIATORS/HOSES)

Forge Motorsport T: 01452 380999.
W: www.forgemotorsport.co.uk

Pacet T: 01628 526754. W: www.pacet.co.uk

Pro Alloy Motorsport T:0845 226 7561. W: www.proalloy.co.uk

Radicool Fabrications T: 01280 701350.
W: www.radicool-fabrications.co.uk

Samco Sport T: 01443 238464. W: www.samcosport.com

Silicon Hoses T: 0845 838 5364. W: www.siliconhoses.com

Viper Performance T: 0845 0953 423. W: www.viper-performance.co.uk

ELECTRICAL/WIRING SUPPLIES

Auto Electric Supplies T: 01584 819552.
W: www.autoelectricsupplies.co.uk

Autocar Electrical T: 0207 4034334. W: www.autocar-electrical.com

Autosparks T: 01423 506133

IEM Services T: 01209 214086. W: www.thewiringproject.co.uk

Vehicle Wiring Products T: 0115 9305454.
W: www.vehicleproducts.co.uk

World of Wiring T: 01782 208050. W: www.blitzworld.co.uk

ENGINE SPECIALISTS/ENGINE PARTS

AB Performance T: 01449 736633. W: www.abperformance.co.uk

Avonbar T: 01279 873428. W: www.avonbar.com

British American Engines T: 01903 521618.
W: www.britishamericanengines.co.uk

Burton Power T: 0208 518 9189. W: www.burtonpower.com

Cambridge Motorsports Parts T: 01462 684300.
W: www.cambridgemotorsport.com

Cat Cams T: 01444 243720. W: www.catcams.co.uk

Dee Ltd T: 01926 311915. W: www.dee-ltd.co.uk

Dunnell Engines T: 01449 677726. W: www.dunnellengines.com

Holeshot Racing T: 028 3882 0026. W: www.holeshotracing.co.uk

ITG T: 024 7630 5386. W: www.itgairfilters.com

LS Power T: 01949 843299. W: www.gdcars.com

Partsworld Performance W: www.partsworldperformance.com

Performance Unlimited T: 01904 489332.
W: www.performanceunlimited.co.uk

Piper Cams T: 01303 245300. W: www.pipercams.co.uk

QEP (Cat Cams) T: 01444 243720. W: www.q-e-p.co.uk

Real Steel T: 01895 440505. W: www.realsteel.co.uk

TTS Performance T: 01327858212. W: www.tts-performance.co.uk

Ultimate Performance T: 01604 771221. W: www.ultimatep.com

Yorkshire Engine Supplies T: 07960 011585.
W: www.yorkshireengines.co.uk

ENGINE MANAGEMENT

Autocar Electrical Equipment (Lumenition) T: 020 7403 4334.
W: www.lumenition.com

KMS T: +31 (0) 402854064. W: www.van-kronenburg.nl

Omex Technology T: 01242 260656. W: www.omextechnology.co.uk

Trigger Wheels E: sales@trigger-wheels.com W: www.trigger-wheels.com

EXHAUST PARTS/FABRICATION

Custom Chrome T: 024 7638 7808. W: www.custom-chrome.co.uk

Simpson Race Exhausts T: 01753 532222.
W: www.simpsonraceexhausts.com

FIBREGLASS REPAIRS

CFS T: 01209 821028 W: cfsnet.co.uk

Dynamic Mouldings T: 01454 222 899.
W: www.dynamicmouldings.co.uk
East Coast Fibreglass T: 0191 497 5134. W: www.ecfibreglass.co.uk
GW-GRP Designs T: 01507 524426.
W: www.gw-grpdesigns.co.uk
Westgate Composites T: 07733 282947.
W: www.westgatecomposites.com

FUEL/OIL/BRAKE FLUID COMPONENTS
BGC T: 01945 466690. W: www.bgcmotorsport.co.uk
Earls T: 01803 869850. W: www.earls.co.uk
Hosetechnik T: 0845 838 5364. W: www.hosetechnik.com

GEARBOX SPECIALISTS
3J Driveline T: 01926 650426. W: www.3jdriveline.com
BGH Geartech T: 01580 714114. W: www.bghgeartech.co.uk
CG Motorsport T: 01132 426359. W: www.clutch-specialists.co.uk
Elite Racing Transmissions T: 07976 487861.
W: www.eliteracingtransmissions.com
MST Developments T: 07890 587531
Quaife T: 01732 741144. W: www.quaife.co.uk
Tran-X T: 01732 741144. W: www.tran-x.com

GEARBOX SPECIALISTS (REVERSE)
Elite Racing Transmissions T: 07976 487861.
W: www.eliteracingtransmissions.com
Lynx AE T: 01908 510000. W: www.lynxae.co.uk
MNR reverse box T: 01423 780196.
W: www.mnrltd.co.uk
Quaife T: 01732 741144. W: www.quaife.co.uk
Westgarage Engineering T: 01383 850480.
W: www.westgarage.co.uk

INSTRUMENT/GAUGE SUPPLIERS
Acewell T: 0191 640 8663. W: www.acewell.co.uk
Digital Speedos T: 07967 676703.
W: www.digitalspeedos.co.uk
ETB Instruments T: 01702 601055. W: www.etbinstruments.com
Race Technology T: 01773 537620. W: www.race-technology.com
Racetech W: www.racetechdesign.com
Revotec T: 01491 824424. W: www.revotec.com
Smiths (via Europa) T: 01283 815609. W: www.europaspares.com
SPA T: 01827 300150. W: www.spa-uk.co.uk
Stack W: www.stackltd.com
Trailtech T: 01896 753111. W: www.trailtech.net

IVA CONTACTS
Download the manual W: http://tinyurl.com/c7d46kh
IVA Test Stations W: http://tinyurl.com/cpz6ppx
Official Website W: www.gov.uk/vehicle-approval/overview

KIT CAR BUILDING SERVICES
Arden Automotive T: 01235 813161.
W: www.ardenautomotive.co.uk
Automotive Solutions and Racing T: 01773 719287.
W: www.kitcar.me.uk
Birch Brothers T: 01274 834921. W: birchbros.org.uk
Thunder Road Cars T: 020 8502 4090. W: www.thunderroadcars.com
Southways Automotive T: 07976 531824.
W: www.southwaysautomotive.co.uk
Sussex Kit Cars T: 01435 812706. E: john@sussexkitcars.co.uk

LIGHTING
SVC T: 08456 581251. W: www.s-v-c.co.uk

MISCELLANEOUS
Aluminium fabrication – Bogg Brothers T: 01944 738234.
W: www.boggbros.co.uk
Aluminium fabrication – Alloy Racing Fabrications T: 01623 835805.
W: www.alloyracingfabrications.com
Carbon Mods T: 01782 324000. W: www.carbonmods.co.uk
Heater – T7 Design T: 07595 975777. W: www.t7design.co.uk
Powdercoating – Electrostatic Magic
W:www.electrostaticmagic.co.uk
Thread repair kits – Uni-Thread T: 01803 867832.
Trailer manufacturers – Aluminium Trailer Company T: 01844 353539.
W: www.allytrailer.co.uk

NUTS, BOLTS & FIXINGS
LBF T: 01263 713498. E: ray@lotusbendit.plus.com

PAINTING/BODYSHOP SERVICES
Auto Mirage T: 01253 734743. W: www.automirage.co.uk
Brooklands Motor Company T: 01932 828545.
W: www.brooklandsmotorcompany.co.uk
IDL UK T: 01424 854900. W: www.idluk.eu
Lee's Bodyshop T: 01332 331764. W: www.leesbodyshop.co.uk
Pinewood Body Repairs T: 01304 203020.
Precision Paint T: 01823 666289 W: www.precisionpaint.co.uk
Southside Accident And Repair Centre T: 020 8317 1111.
W: www.southsidearc.com

SMS Autospray T: 01406 371504. W: www.smsautospray.co.uk
Specialised Paintwork T: 0118 930 6206.
W: www.specialisedpaintwork.com
The Colourworx T: 01637 873218. W: www.thecolourworx.co.uk

PARTS SUPPLIERS (GENERAL BROCHURE)
Burton Power T: 020 8518 9189. W: www.burtonpower.com
Cambridge Motorsport Parts T: 01462 684300.
W: www.cambridgemotorsport.com
Car Builder Solutions T: 01580 891309. W: www.cbsonline.co.uk
Demon Tweeks T: 0845 330 4751. W: www.demon-tweeks.co.uk
Europa Spares T: 01283 815609. W: www.europaspares.com
Furore T: 07905 897407. W: www.forurecars.co.uk
Kit Parts Direct T: 07895 864500. W: www.kitpartsdirect.com
Machine Mart T: 0844 8801250. W: www.machinemart.co.uk
Merlin Motorsport T: 01249 782101.
W: www.merlinmotorsport.co.uk
Rally Design T: 01227 792792. W: www.rallydesign.co.uk
Richbrook W: www.richbrook-styling.co.uk

PROPSHAFT SERVICES
Autoprop T: 01342 322623. W: www.autoprop-uk.co.uk
Bailey Morris T: 01480 216250. W: www.baileymorris.co.uk
CPS Drivelink T: 0191 4821690. W: www.drivelink.com
Dunning & Fairbank T: 0113 248 8788. W: www.dandfltd.co.uk
Reco-Prop T: 01582 412110. W: www.reco-prop.com

REGISTRATION
Official Website W: http://tinyurl.com/czl89bx
INF26 Leaflet W: http://tinyurl.com/ygk8wqv

RUST PREVENTION
GEP T: 07809 686788. E: pyne79@yahoo.com
Electrostatic Magic W: www.electrostaticmagic.co.uk
KBS Rustseal T: 01803 527961. W: www.therustshop.com

ROLLING ROAD/SUSPENSION TUNING
Atspeed T: 01268 773377. W: www.atspeedracing.co.uk
Daytuner Performance T: 01423 523323. W: www.daytuner.co.uk
John Clarkson Autos T: 01257 263879. E: ajcmimi@tiscali.co.uk
Northampton Motorsport T: 01604 766624.
W: www.northamptonmotorsport.com
Track Developments T: 01666 840482. W: www.trackdevelopments.co.uk

SEAT MANUFACTURERS/SUPPLIERS
Cobra Seats T: 01952 684020. W: www.cobraseats.com
Corbeau Seats T: 01424 854499. W: www.corbeau-seats.co.uk
Intatrim T: 01952 608608. W: www.intatrimtelford.co.uk
Interiors Seating T: 01623 400660. W: www.interiorsseating.co.uk
JK Composites T: 01704 569730. W: www.jkcomposites.com
Tillett Racing Seats T: 01795 420312. W: www.tillett.co.uk

SUSPENSION COMPONENTS
Dampertech T: 01709 703992. W: www.dampertech.co.uk
Protech Shocks T: 01225 705553. W: www.protechshocks.co.uk
Supaflex T: 01749 678152. W: www.superflex.co.uk

TOOL SUPPLIERS
Draper T: 023 8049 4333. W: www.draper.co.uk/ckc
Milli-Grip T: 01273 494844. W: www.milli-grip.com
Memfast T: 01386 556868. W: www.memfast.co.uk
Perm-Grit Tools T: 0800 298 5121. W: www.permagrit.com

TRIM SERVICES
Cartlidge Coach Trimming T: 0121 558 9135.
W: www.cctrim.co.uk
Gabbat & Brown T: 01704 821105.
W: www.gabbatandbrown.co.uk
M&M Classic Car Components T: 01775 762004.
W: www.m-mclassiccartrim.com
Seals+Direct T: 0845 226 3345. W: www.sealsplusdirect.co.uk
Woolies T: 01778 347347. W: www.woolies-trim.co.uk

WHEEL SUPPLIERS
BK Racing W: www.bkracing.co.uk
Compomotive T: 01902 311499. W: www.comp.co.uk
Force Racing T: 0113 252 5507. W: www.force-racing.co.uk
Hawk Cars T: 01892 750282. W: www.hawkcars.co.uk
Image Wheels T: 0121 522 2442. W: www.imagewheels.co.uk
John Brown Wheels W: www.johnbrownwheels.com
Midland Wheels T: 01926 817444. W: www.midlandwheels.com
Momo T: 01268 764411. W: www.momo-uk.co.uk
Performance Wheels T: 01530 517920.
W: www.performwheels.co.uk
Team Dynamics W: w§ww.team-dynamics.com
TSW T: 01908 625625. W: www.tsw-wheels.co.uk
Wolfrace W: www.wolfrace.co.uk

Design And Build A Sports Car – Stuart Mills